PR
EL

Other Titles of Interest

227	Beginners Guide to Building Electronic Projects
BP44	IC555 Projects
BP88	How to Use Op-amps
BP110	How to Get Your Electronic Projects Working
BP121	How to Design and Make Your Own PCB's
BP240	Remote Control Handbook
BP266	Electronic Modules and Systems for Beginners
BP273	Practical Electronic Sensors
BP299	Practical Electronic Filters
BP321	Circuit Source – Book 1
BP322	Circuit Source – Book 2
BP324	The Art of Soldering
BP332	A Beginners Guide to TTL Digital ICs
BP333	A Beginners Guide to CMOS Digital ICs
BP335	Operational Amplifier User's Handbook
BP345	Getting Started in Practical Electronics

PRACTICAL ELECTRONIC TIMING

by

Owen Bishop

BERNARD BABANI (publishing) LTD
THE GRAMPIANS
SHEPHERDS BUSH ROAD
LONDON W6 7NF
ENGLAND

Please Note

Although every care has been taken with the production of this book to ensure that any projects, designs, modifications and/or programs etc. contained herewith, operate in a correct and safe manner and also that all components specified are normally available in Great Britain, the Publishers and Author do not accept responsibility in any way for the failure, including fault in design, of any project, design, modification or program to work correctly or to cause damage to any other equipment that it may be connected to or used in conjunction with, or in respect of any other damage or injury that may be so caused, nor do the Publishers accept responsibility in any way for the failure to obtain specified components.

Notice is also given that if equipment that is still under warranty is modified in any way or used or connected with home-built equipment then that warranty may be void.

First Published – October 1993

British Library Cataloguing in Publication Data:
Bishop, O. N.
Practical Electronic Timing
1. Title
621.381

ISBN 0 85934 317 0

Printed and Bound in Great Britain by Cox & Wyman Ltd, Reading

Warning

Certain circuits and projects included in this book can involve mains voltages and wiring. These are not recommended for beginners or those with little knowledge or experience of working with mains wiring and voltages.

Preface

This is a book of practical electronic timing circuits, employing several different kinds of specialized integrated circuit. It is essentially a project book, but each group of projects is introduced by a discussion which highlights some of the problems of timekeeping and the ways they may be solved by electronic means.

In addition, the book includes a chapter on using or adapting ready-made timer modules and on using the electronics from digital clocks or watches.

The projects have been selected so that they are of interest to the hobbyist, with many applications in and around the home. Many of the circuits are presented in such a way that they can readily be adapted to tailor them to the reader's requirements. This also means that the circuits are of help for students who have to design and build a project for examination purposes.

To assist the reader in choosing projects, they are divided into three categories of difficulty:

Beginner's projects – any person who has built one or two projects from simple kits should be able to tackle these. Many of them can be built in a single evening.

Average projects – the beginner will soon graduate to projects at this level.

Advanced projects – usually the circuits require experience and skill in laying out the circuit board and have rather more connections than usual.

Each project description begins with an outline of the function of the circuit and the principles on which it operates. Then follows a detailed account of the way the circuit works. This will be found helpful when checking the completed project for correct action. Finally, under the heading *Construction*, we deal with suitable power supplies (all projects will operate from batteries), enclosures, special aspects of construction, and indicate how to test the project at each stage of assembly. Beginners will find that some of the books listed under "Other Titles of Interest", at the front of this book, will help them with basic constructional techniques, which are not dealt with here. One or more circuit diagrams accompanies every project description.

Owen Bishop

Contents

Page

Chapter 1
TIME – PAST AND PRESENT 1
Electric Clocks and Watches 2
Atomic Clocks 3
The Time of Day 5

Chapter 2
MEASURING REAL TIME 9
Quartz Crystal Oscillators 9
CMOS Crystal Oscillators 12
Frequency Division 13
Real Time 14
Projects for Measuring Real Time
Project 1 – Real Time Clock 15
The basic clock 18
Expansions (a) Alarm output 26
(b) Seconds display 33
(c) Day of week display 33
(d) Time recorder 33
(e) Periodic trigger 41
(f) Data logger 43
Project 2 – Simple Data Logger 50
Project 3 – Striking Clock 52

Chapter 3
MEASURING ELAPSED TIME 65
Time Keeping with Capacitors 68
Longer Periods 71
High Precision 73
Off Air Timing 76
Projects For Measuring Elapsed Time
Project 4 – Audible Timer 77
Project 5 – Long Interval Alarm Timer 81
Project 6 – Easy Analogue Timer 86
Project 7 – Yoga/Exercise Timer 91
Project 8 – Reaction Timer 93
Project 9 – Off Air Frequency Receiver 97

Chapter 3 (Continued) **Page**
Project 10 – Priority Timer 103
Project 11 – Lap Timer 105
Project 12 – Low Cost Minutes Timer 110
Project 13 – Minutes/Seconds Timer With
Module Display 114
Project 14 – Stop Clocks 118
Project 15 – Metronome 124
Project 16 – Count Down Timer 128
Project 17 – Simple Precision Timer 133
Project 18 – Relay Delay Timer 137

Chapter 4
USING CLOCK MODULES 143
Timing With a Clock Module 144
Using the Buzzer Output 148
Timing With a Digital Clock or Watch 158

Appendix
TERMINAL CONNECTIONS 160

Chapter 1

TIME – PAST AND PRESENT

One of the strangest things about time is that no one really knows what it is. But we are all agreed on certain aspects of it, such as that time is something which passes. We proceed from the past to the present and on to the future. This is referred to as the *arrow of time*. Although many fascinating stories have been written about travelling through time, this still remains in the realms of fiction. Or does it? According to certain theories, electrons and photons are able on occasions to travel *backward* in time. Such bizarre happenings and their implications are well outside our everyday experience and, in spite of all the theorising, the nature of time remains a mystery.

The curious thing is that, although we do not know what time is, we are able to measure time much more precisely than we can measure length, mass, temperature or any other physical quantity. Measurement of time began in the distant past when people first started to recognise that one season follows another and that the cycle is repeated annually. The first measures of time were the natural ones, the year, the month and the day. These natural periods are sufficient for many purposes, but the division of the day into a number of hours and then into minutes and seconds allows our activities to be timed with increasing precision. The ancients measured periods of the order of hours by using sundials, or by a device known as a water-clock or *clepsydra*. The clepsydra consists of a vessel with a small hole in the bottom. Its interior surface is marked with rings to measure the amount of water remaining in the vessel. The vessel is filled with water and, as the water runs out through the hole, the surface comes level with each ring in succession, thus measuring the time elapsed. Although this may not seem to be an accurate way of measuring time, it was good enough to be used by Galileo when studying the acceleration of falling objects, in this case a ball rolling down a slight slope.

The essential point about the clepsydra is that it measures time by making use of a *physical property*, in this case a physical property of water. Various forms of clepsydra were in use for thousands of years. The hour-glass (or sand-glass) is another ancient instrument that relies upon a physical property for measuring time. Mechanical clocks also rely on physical events, such as the period of swing of a pendulum, or the period of oscillation of a balance wheel. We are not concerned with the details of mechanical clocks here except to say that it was the increased interest in exploration by sea that generated the rapid improvement in this technology during the last few hundred years.

Mechanical clocks of the 13th Century were precise only to about 1000 seconds per day. This would have been no use to a mariner trying to establish the longitude of his ship. By the early 18th Century, many improvements in design had been achieved, and John Harrison produced the first of his highly accurate clocks (known as *chronometers*) especially for use on board ship. The best of these had a precision of 4.5s in 10 weeks (64ms per day). Several of these chronometers are still working and keeping accurate time today.

Electric Clocks and Watches

In the early clepsydras, the passage of time was noted by observing the level of the water against the rings marked inside the bowl of the instrument. Later versions had a float attached to a cord which was wound round a cylinder. As the water level fell, the cord made the cylinder rotate. There was a pointer fixed to the cylinder and the rotating cylinder caused the pointer to turn over a dial graduated in hours. In short, they had a *mechanical system* to couple the timing device to a display, making it easier to read the time. Similarly, the mechanical clock had a chain of gear wheels between the timing mechanism and the hand or hands which indicated the time on the dial. In some of these the gear chain was extremely elaborate, with dials to indicate the day of the week, the date, and even the phases of the Moon.

In the earliest electric clocks, produced in the 19th Century, the gear chain was replaced partly by an electric circuit. Usually the movement of the pendulum or balance wheel was sensed by electromagnetic means. The pulses so generated were used to drive the hands, as well as to provide impulses to the pendulum or balance wheel to keep it in oscillation. There were many designs, but most suffered from the defect of using mechanical switching, with the attendant problems of contact wear and corrosion. The key to further improvement came when electronic amplifiers were developed in the early 20th Century and the first truly *electronic* as opposed to *electrical* clocks were designed. However, with improvement of contact materials and in ways of minimising contact corrosion, electrical clocks continued in use for several decades into the 20th Century. It was not until the invention of the transistor that electronic clocks began to appear on the domestic scene. Even today there are battery-driven *electric* clocks which are essentially mechanical in their timing method (usually a balance wheel) and make use of electricity only to power an electric motor to rewind the spring of the clock occasionally. Another popular type of electric clock has a synchronous motor which uses the 50Hz mains to keep it running at constant speed.

With the advent of transistors the way became open to develop electronically maintained clocks. Amplifying circuits were used to provide power to drive the display mechanism and maintain the pendulum or balance wheel in oscillation, while requiring the minimum of energy from the pendulum or balance wheel itself. Some designs of clock were based on the electronically maintained oscillations of a tuning fork.

However, all of these instruments basically relied on the same mechanical devices that had been in use for centuries – the pendulum, the balance wheel and other mechanical oscillating systems. The next big step forward in everyday timekeeping came with the development of the crystal-based oscillator, which we shall discuss in more detail in Chapter 2.

Atomic Clocks

While the developments outlined in the previous section were in train, an entirely different technique of time-keeping was developed at the National Physical Laboratory and certain other scientific institutions. The atomic clock makes use of the oscillations inherent in the structure and behaviour of atoms and is therefore beyond the influence of temperature, barometric pressure, corrosion and other factors which adversely affect the precision of other types of clock.

Atomic clocks can be based on atoms of various elements but today's practical atomic clocks mostly derive their time-keeping from atoms of caesium. The electrons of an atom orbit around the nucleus at different distances from it. When an electron is supplied with energy by irradiating it with electro-magnetic radiation (e.g. light) of a particular wave-length, the electron gains energy and jumps to an orbit further from the nucleus. Conversely, when an electron jumps from an outer orbit to one closer to the nucleus, it loses energy. This energy appears as an emission of electromagnetic radiation, typically as light of a particular frequency. Since there are only a given number of possible orbits in the atom of an element there are only a limited number of possible orbit jumps and therefore only a limited number of possible frequencies of emissions. This is why the spectrum of an element is not a continuous range of colours but consists of a number of thin lines of different colours.

Jumping from orbit to orbit produces radiation with frequencies in and around the range of the visible spectrum. These frequencies are too high to be coupled into an electronic circuit and used as the basis of time-keeping. However, there is another type of energy change. This results from the *direction* of spin of the electrons. The caesium atom has just one electron in its outermost electron shell and this may exist in one of two states, depending upon the direction it is spinning in. It can flip from one state to the other, either absorbing or emitting energy as it does so. The energy change is less than in jumping from orbit to orbit and so the frequency of the emitted radiation is lower. The frequency lies in the microwave band, which is a region in which electronic circuits can operate.

In one of the most successful types of clock, solid caesium is heated in an oven which has an aperture to allow the caesium to escape as a beam. The beam contains caesium atoms in both magnetic states; the two states are separated from each other by passing the beam through a magnetic field. Atoms of the higher energy state are diverted but those in the other (lower-energy) state pass on to the next stage. This is a microwave cavity into which microwaves of a given frequency are radiated. If the radiation is of exactly the right frequency, atoms are excited to change to the higher energy magnetic state. The more closely the radiation approaches the correct frequency, the higher the proportion of atoms which change state. The generator producing the microwaves is actually a quartz crystal oscillator (page 11) which is tunable over a range of frequencies close to that required to excite the caesium atoms.

As the beam emerges from the microwave cavity it passes through another magnetic field where those atoms that have changed state are separated from those that have not. The beam passes to an atom detector which determines the proportion of atoms that have changed state. This information is fed back to the microwave oscillator, which is tuned automatically to produce the greatest number of atoms of changed (higher-energy) state. The frequency of the oscillator is then known to be exactly that which corresponds to the absorption of energy by the electrons of the caesium atoms. This frequency is known very precisely and is defined as exactly 9 192 631 770Hz. The frequency at which the microwave oscillator is working is divided electronically to produce lower frequencies, which can then be used to operate electronic time-keeping circuits.

Caesium clocks are precise to within 100ns per day (1s per ten million days). They are far more precise than is required for everyday time-keeping. This fact and the great expense of building and operating them means that their use has been restricted to scientific laboratories, even though the first atomic clock was first put into commission as long ago as 1952. As explained in Project 9, frequencies generated by atomic clocks are made available by broadcasting radio signals which can be picked up and received by anyone who has need of this degree of precision.

The Time of Day

There are two aspects to measuring time. One is to measure the length of time between one instant and another. For example, we may start a clock as a runner begins a lap of the race-track and stop it when he crosses the finishing line. This measures *elapsed time.* The second aspect of measuring time is when we want to identify each instant of time according to a fixed time-scale, such as Greenwich Mean Time. As I write this sentence, I can hear the grandfather clock in the hall striking 4 o'clock. I know that (plus or minus a few seconds) the time is 1600hrs GMT on 25 February 1993. This instant of time has now passed and will not occur again. It was a unique point in time.

The second aspect of time is often referred to by computer programmers as *real-time* and, for want of a better term, we will adopt that term in this book. There are a number of related systems for defining real-time. GMT, otherwise known as *Universal Time* is determined by measuring the transits of certain stars (including the Sun) across the meridian. The difficulty with this is that the Earth does not rotate at a constant rate. Its rate varies by a millisecond or more per day. A more recently defined time scale is Ephemeris Time, which is obtained by averaging out the variations in the Earth's rotation over a long period. At present, a second of ET is the average length of the second during the whole of the 19th Century. This gives a very precise figure (1 in 10^9), but there is always the problem that long-term variations in the Earth's rotation may make the 20th Century ET second different from this.

Now that we have highly precise atomic clocks it makes sense to use these as the standard. The present system is to use Universal Coordinated Time (UTC), which runs side-by-side with UT. The correction is based on the second generated by an atomic clock (the time taken for 9 192 631 770 oscillations of the microwave oscillator). The atomic minute is sixty atomic seconds and the atomic hour is sixty atomic minutes, and so on. This atomic time scale is compared with UT and, whenever the two systems differ by more than 0.5s, an adjustment is made to UTC by inserting or removing a second. This is referred to as a *leap-second* by analogy with the extra day that we insert into a leap year. This reduces the difference between UTC and atomic time to less than 0.5s. The two systems then run side-by-side until they differ by more than 0.5s again.

The high precision of atomic clocks has made it possible to confirm some of the effects predicted by the Theory of Relativity. One of these is that time runs more slowly in a strong gravitational field. This effect has been measured by several experiments. In one of these, a hydrogen atomic clock (one that uses hydrogen atoms instead of caesium atoms) was launched by rocket to an altitude of 9600km above the Earth's surface. It was found that this clock gained a billionth of a second per second when compared with an identical clock on the ground. The relatively stronger gravitational field at the Earth's surface made the ground-based clock run slow, relative to the clock at higher altitude. Note that this is *not* an effect of gravity on the atoms of the clocks. It is an effect acting on time itself. To an observer on the ground, the ground-based clock is running at the correct rate. Had there been an observer in the rocket it would have seemed to that person that the rocket-based clock was also running correctly. It is just that the time passes at a slower rate in the vicinity of a massive body such as the Earth.

Another effect is that time appears to run more slowly when a clock or other object is moving. The effect is too small to be noticable as an everyday experience but, when the speed approaches that of the speed of light, the effect is dramatic. This effect has been observed with muons which are short-lived particles created in the upper atmosphere by the impact of cosmic rays. Although the muons travel at high speed, they decay so rapidly that they would disappear after travelling an average of 600m. None of them would reach the ground. But in fact they manage to travel much further than this. Because they are travelling at speeds approaching the speed of light, time runs very slowly for them; they live up to 9 times longer (as measured by *our* time). Similarly, a person travelling at that speed would age 9 times as slowly. For a photon leaving a distant star and travelling to Earth at the speed of light, time stands still. It leaves the star and reaches the Earth at the same instant in its own life.

Time is truly strange but that does not prevent us from building electronic clocks and other devices for marking its passage. The rest of the book is devoted to these practical aspects of time-keeping.

Chapter 2

MEASURING REAL TIME

In Chapter 1 we saw how any timing device relies on a physical process or device that is known to run at a constant or predictably variable rate. It might be the flow of water through an orifice, as in the clepsydra, or the swinging of a pendulum, as in clocks of very many kinds. The development of electrical clocks, in which the physical device (usually mechanical) is linked to the display by electrical or electronic means is an improvement on the purely mechanical clock but there are problems in coupling the mechanical and electrical parts. Electronic clocks, in which the oscillating mechanism is itself electronic, overcome these problems and make the clock more reliable. The crystal clock is by far the most successful of the electronic clocks, but other electronic timing devices may have applications in certain circumstances. In this chapter we outline the way in which the crystal clock works and describe several practical projects based on this. Other timing techniques are described in Chapter 3.

Quartz Crystal Oscillators

A major step in the development of electronic clocks and watches was the use of quartz crystal oscillators. Quartz is a hard crystalline form of silicon dioxide. A crystal consists of atoms of silicon and oxygen arranged in a regular though complicated array, the matrix. The regular structure of the matrix gives rise to the regular shape of the natural quartz crystal. In the crystal, atoms of silicon share some of their outer electrons with adjacent oxygen atoms. As a consequence, the silicon atoms become positively charged and the oxygen atoms become negatively charged. The resulting electrostatic attraction holds the silicon and oxygen atoms together in the matrix.

If the crystal is subjected to mechanical stress, the matrix becomes distorted. The distances between neighbouring atoms remains unaltered but the orientation of the atoms with respect to each other becomes altered. The relative displacement of positively charged silicon atoms and negatively charged oxygen atoms gives rise to an electrostatic field. One surface of the crystal becomes positively charged with respect to the other. Conversely, if an electric field is applied across a slice of crystal, electrostatic forces distort the matrix and the crystal changes shape. This relationship between crystal shape and electric field is known as the *piezo-electric effect.* The effect is observed in crystals of many different substances, but quartz has been the one most used in time-keeping.

The direct link between mechanical vibration and electrical field makes the quartz crystal much simpler to use than a pendulum or vibrating tuning fork. For use in a quartz crystal oscillator, a specially-cut slice of quartz is coated on opposite surfaces with a metallic layer. It thus has the *physical* structure of a capacitor, as suggested by its symbol in circuit diagrams (Fig. 2.1), though *electrically* the crystal itself behaves more like an inductor. The crystal is connected into a resonant circuit (Fig. 2.2) in which there is amplification and feedback. If the resonant frequency of the circuit is the same as that of the natural mechanical resonance of the crystal, there is a mutually reinforcing interaction between the crystal and the circuit. The vibrations of the crystal are maintained by the oscillation of the circuit and the resulting alternating p.d. across the crystal maintains the circuit in a state of oscillation.

Electrically, the crystal has the same properties as a series RLC circuit in parallel with a capacitor. The combination of series and parallel resonance results in a rapid change in impedance and phase angle at frequencies just above and just below the resonant frequency. In other words, the crystal has

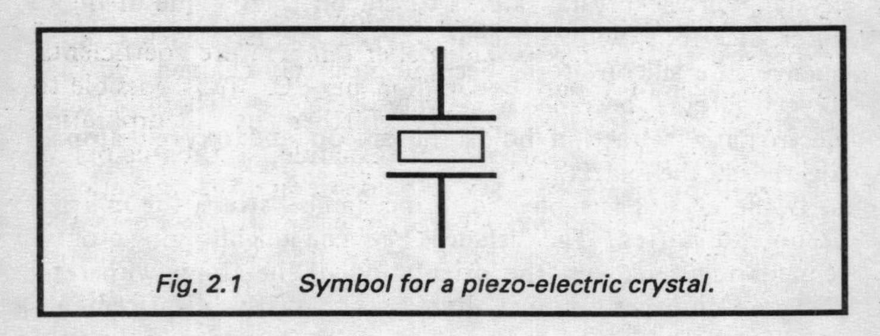

Fig. 2.1 Symbol for a piezo-electric crystal.

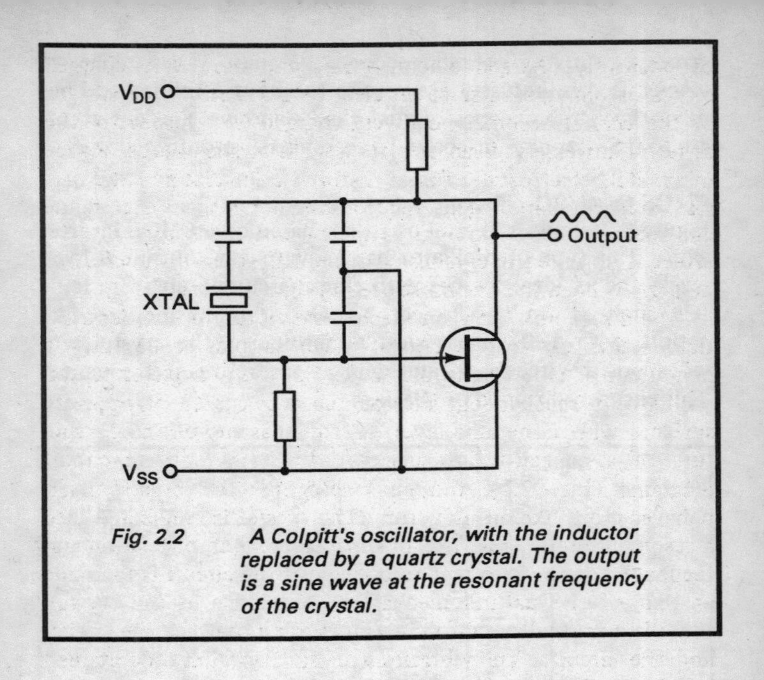

Fig. 2.2 *A Colpitt's oscillator, with the inductor replaced by a quartz crystal. The output is a sine wave at the resonant frequency of the crystal.*

a high Q. Consequently, the oscillator circuit resonates strongly at the natural frequency of the crystal but not at slightly higher or lower frequencies. It is thus ideal as a timing device. Crystals can be cut to oscillate at frequencies in the range 10kHz to 10MHz, with a high degree of precision, and at very low cost.

Crystal clocks have the additional advantage of high temperature stability, a change of less than 0.00001% per degree Celsius being typical of low-cost crystals. More expensive crystals have even smaller temperature coefficients, of the order of 1 part per million per °C. It is possible to improve temperature stability further by incorporating temperature compensation (for example, a thermistor) in the oscillator or by enclosing the crystal in a thermostatically controlled compartment. Before the use of caesium clocks for this purpose, crystal clocks were used as time standards. They were manufactured to a high degree of precision, with errors of only a few microseconds per day. Less expensive clocks used in industry are precise to about 1 millisecond per day. Even the cheapest digital clocks and watches are accurate to 0.5s per day, or about 15 seconds per month.

CMOS Crystal Oscillator

Figure 2.3 shows a crystal oscillator based on a CMOS inverter gate. This type of oscillator has a square-wave output at logic levels and is ideal for use with clock circuits built from logic ICs, such as that of Project 1. Owing to its inductor-like action, with 180° phase shift at resonance, the crystal provides positive feedback and gain at the resonant frequency. This ensures sustained oscillation.

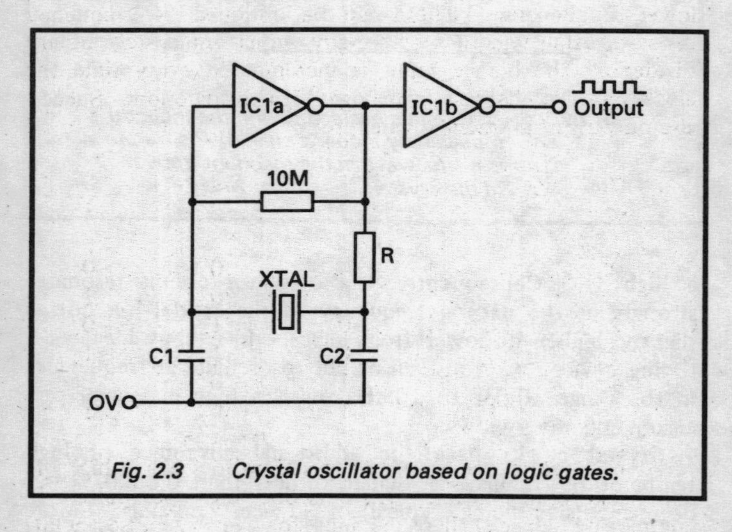

Fig. 2.3 Crystal oscillator based on logic gates.

The inverter of this oscillator (IC1a) may be a single INVERT gate, or may be a NAND or NOR gate with its input terminals connected together to make it act as an inverter. The total load capacitance is C1 and C2 in series plus up to 10pF due to stray capacitance. C2 can be a variable capacitance if it is required to trim the frequency precisely; otherwise C2 is about three times C1. The total load capacitance is usually 30pF, depending on the type of crystal. A suitable value for R is 10kΩ. The 4060 IC used in Project 1 has some of the oscillator circuitry built-in, so that only the crystal, the capacitors and resistor R need to be provided.

Figure 2.3 is a parallel-resonant circuit, and the crystal used should be one cut for this mode of operation. Series-resonant circuits are sometimes used and require a different type of crystal.

Frequency Division

The natural frequency of vibration of a small slice of quartz is necessarily very high, of the order of kilohertz or megahertz. Although high frequencies may be used directly in radio-frequency circuits, time-keeping usually requires much lower frequencies. These can be obtained by frequency division, using logic ICs. Normally we use multi-stage binary dividers. The binary input is incremented every time the clock input is changed from logic high to logic low. Successive outputs of a 3-stage divider are:

Pulse No.	*Stage* 3	2	1
0	0	0	0
1	0	0	1
2	0	1	0
3	0	1	1
4	1	0	0
5	1	0	1

At each pulse, the input changes from low (0) to high (1) and back to low again. There is one 'high' per pulse. In comparison, stage 1 has one high for every 2 pulses, while stage 2 has one high for every 4 pulses. The frequency of the output from stage 1 is exactly half that of the input, and the frequency of the output of stage 2 is exactly half that of stage 1, and so on. A chain such as this divides the frequency by 2 at every stage. Given an input frequency of 32.768kHz and a fifteen-stage counter, the frequency is divided by 2^{15} (which equals 32 768) to give a signal of exactly 1Hz from the output of the 15th stage. Crystals are manufactured with this frequency for use in clocks and watches. The 1Hz signal provides the 1-second pulses for driving a seconds clock. Divided by 10 this gives tens of seconds and further stages of division yield minutes, tens of minutes, hours and so on. Project 1 illustrates a complete dividing chain of this kind. It is also possible to use a 4.194 304MHz crystal and a 22-stage divider.

The previous table also shows that the outputs of the stages, taken together, are equivalent to the pulse number expressed in binary digits. The IC counts the number of pulses received from the oscillator. Thus an identical chain of ICs can also be used as a counter, and frequency-division ICs are also known as counter ICs.

Real Time

Clocks based on the crystal oscillator are suitable for measuring both real-time and elapsed time. Project 13 is an example of measuring elapsed time with a crystal clock. To measure real time we need some means of synchronising the clock with a time standard. Probably the most well-known time standard is the Greenwich time signal (the 'pips') transmitted by radio all over the World. This time signal is generated by the second most accurate clock in the World, situated in the basement of Broadcasting House, London. Rather more local time signals are the 'guns' fired from prominent places at prescribed times. An example is the gun fired from the battlements of Edinburgh Castle at 1pm every weekday. Time signals such as these are accurate enough for the setting of clocks and watches for everyday time-keeping.

Greater accuracy is needed for certain types of scientific observation. Astronomers in different parts of the World need to be able to work to a common time system so that observations made at different places may be correlated. Similarly, it is essential for seismographs to operate to a precise time scale so that events below the Earth's surface may be precisely located. There are several dozen radio stations throughout the World which continuously broadcast precise time signals in coded form, derived from atomic clocks. In Britain, time data is broadcast from the MSF station at Rugby.

Although the quartz crystal clock is accurate enough for very many purposes, it has limitations. For one thing, moderately priced crystals have a tolerance of about ±20 parts per million, which means that they are possibly in error by as much as ±1.7s per day. There is also the problem of temperature coefficient. The natural period of vibration of the crystal varies with the cube of the temperature. At temperatures around 25°C, the coefficient is very small. Fortunately, this is the region in which most clocks and watches are required to keep time. But a crystal exposed to temperatures below 0°C and higher than 50°C shows a marked temperature effect which rapidly gets even worse at lower and higher temperatures. It can amount to 100 ppm or more, equivalent to several seconds a day. For clocks intended to operate in low or high temperatures, it is preferable to use an atomic clock or a broadcast time standard, as in Project 9.

Projects For Measuring Real Time

Project 1 – Real Time Clock

(Advanced project)

This project is a flexible one which can be added to in stages. It starts as a straightforward crystal-driven clock, with a display of hours and minutes, and a flashing LED for counting seconds. The circuit is expandable so that you can add further facilities as and when you need them, or when you can afford either the time or the cost of adding them. The expansions are:

(a) Alarm (buzzer) output
(b) Display seconds
(c) Display day of the week
(d) Record the times at which a given event occurs
(e) Programmable output to signal every minute, every hour, or at any other regular interval (periodic trigger)
(f) Record input data at regular intervals (data logger).

Thus the clock has many applications as a data recorder as well as for simply telling the time. If all you will ever need is a simple timepiece, you will find it cheaper to buy a factory-made clock. These are mass-produced at very low prices.

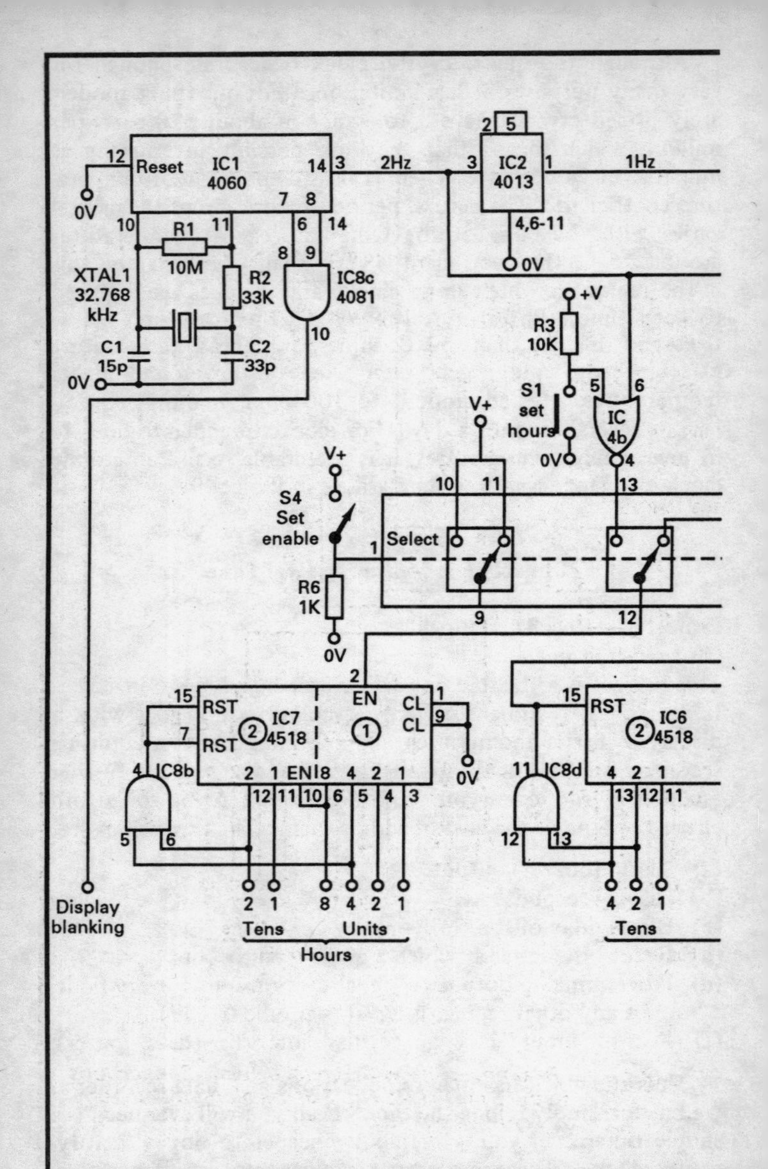
12
Reset
IC1
4060
14
3
2Hz
3
IC2
4013
1
1Hz
2
5
0V
7
8
10
R1
11
6
14
4,6-11
0V
10M
8
9
XTAL1
32.768
kHz
R2
33K
IC8c
4081
C1
15p
C2
33p
10
0V
+V
R3
10K
S1
set
hours
5
6
IC
4b
0V
4
V+
V+
S4
Set
enable
10
11
13
Select
1
R6
1K
0V
9
12
2
15
RST
IC7
4518
EN
CL
CL
1
9
7
RST
0V
4
IC8b
2
1
EN
8
4
2
1
12
11
10
6
5
4
3
5
6
15
RST
IC6
4518
11
IC8d
4
2
1
13
12
11
12
13
Display
blanking
2
1
8
4
2
1
Tens
Units
Hours
4
2
1
Tens

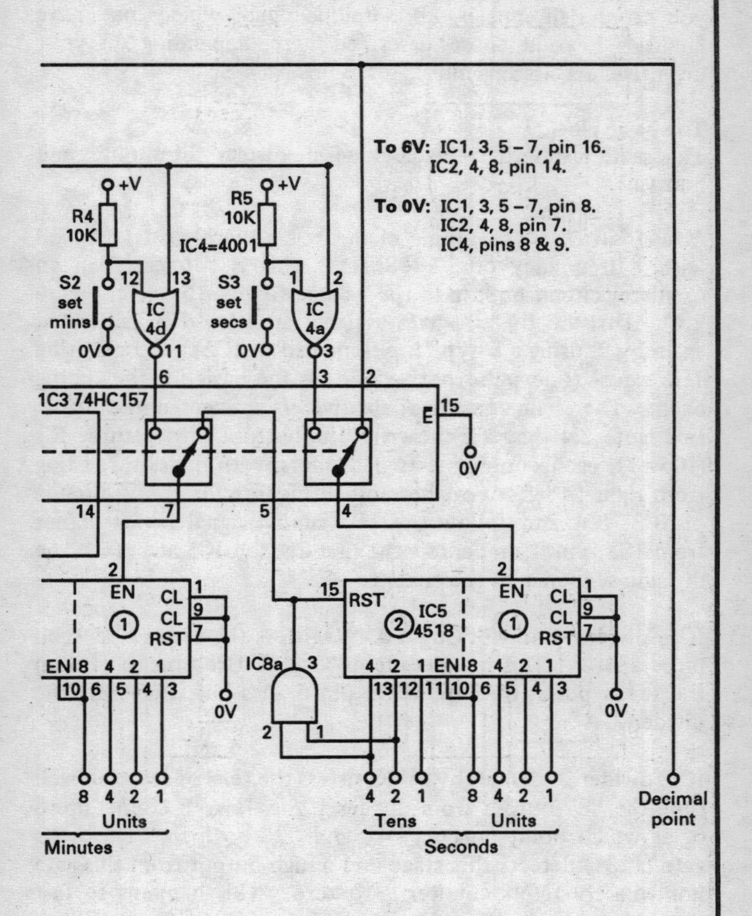

Fig. 2.4 *Real-time clock with digital display. Connections to the display (see Fig. 2.5) are along the bottom edge of the diagram.*

Alternatively, you can begin with a ready-made clock module, as described in Chapter 4. But this project opens the way for you to design and build a unique clock which may have facilities beyond those described here, depending on your inventiveness and ingenuity.

The basic clock

This section describes the clock with a display for minutes and hours.

How it works: The timing element is a piezo-electric crystal with a frequency of 32.768kHz. This is connected in an oscillator circuit built in to the 14-stage divider IC (IC1, Figure 2.4). Division by 2^{14} gives a signal at 2Hz. This is divided again by 2, using a D-type flip-flop (half of IC2). The resulting 1Hz signal (one pulse per second) is the basis for the timing chain. The chain consists of six dividers connected in cascade. In Figure 2.4 they are shown in the bottom row as three ICs (IC5–7), each containing two dividers, with division running from right to left. For the moment, ignore the gating circuits of IC3–IC4 and follow the 1Hz timing signal which comes from IC3, pin 4, and enters the first divider, IC5 at pin 2. The division sequence of the chain is:

IC5, divider 1: divides by 10. Registers the seconds as each pulse arrives. This is a decade divider so it returns to zero on the tenth pulse; output "8" at pin 6 goes low, triggering the divider 2.

IC5, divider 2: divides by 6. Registers the tens of seconds each time the "8" output from divider 1 goes low. It counts up to 6, at which point outputs "4" and "2" go high. The AND gate (IC8a) detects this stage and a high output from this gate immediately resets counter 2 to zero. This happens so fast that the output apparently changes from 5 to 0. Thus dividers 1 and 2, count seconds from 00 to 59, returning to 00 at the end of each minute.

IC6, dividers 1 and 2: This IC is wired in the same way as IC5 and works in the same way, registering minutes from 00 to 59.

IC7, divider 1: divides by 10. It registers hours and, as it returns to zero the low-going "8" output triggers divider 2 to register tens of hours.

IC7, divider 2: Resetting is different on this IC. When divider 2 has reached a count of 2 and divider 1 has reached a count of 4, the "2" output of divider 2 and the "4" output of divider 1 are both high. The output of the AND gate IC8b goes high and resets *both* dividers instantly. The result of this is that the divider apparently registers hours from 00 to 23 before returning to zero. This gives the clock its 24-hour display.

Figure 2.5 shows connections to the display circuit for each IC. If you are building the clock in its simplest form, the connections from IC5 to the display are omitted. It is not possible to omit IC5 itself, for this is a necessary part of the dividing chain.

The prototype was built using 0.3in *low-current* displays, which are of a convenient size for most purposes, but there is no reason why larger displays should not be used. If the display is not of the low current type, or the operating voltage is greater than 6V, it is essential to wire a series resistor between the LED segments and each output terminal of the decoders. Typically, these resistors should be 180Ω. In this case, the blanking input (see later) is not required and pins 8 and 9 of IC8 are connected to 0V or +V. With the very largest displays (2in or more) each segment may consist of several LEDs, in which case the manufacturer may recommend that the power supply be uprated to 12V. This circuit can not be operated at voltages as high as this. Two-digit and four-digit LED displays are available with common connections to the same segments in each digit. Such displays are known as *multiplexed* displays and special circuitry is required to drive them. Such displays can not be used with this clock circuit.

The clock can also be used with a liquid crystal (LCD) display, with some modifications to the wiring. Figure 2.6 shows how to use a 74HC4543 decoder in place of the 4511. The AND gate IC8c is not required, and its inputs are connected either to 0V or the positive supply. Using an LCD

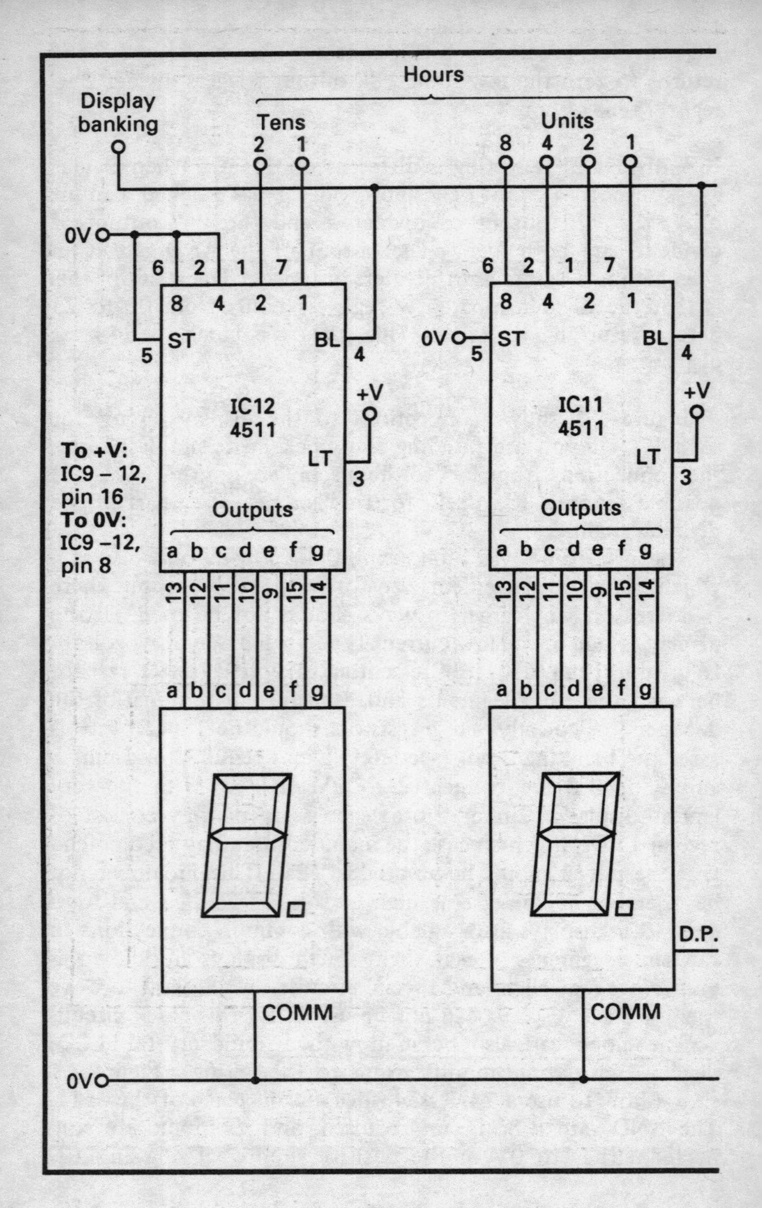
Hours
Display banking
Tens
2 1
Units
8 4 2 1
0V
6 2 1 7
8 4 2 1
ST
BL
5
4
+V
IC12
4511
LT
3
To +V:
IC9 – 12,
pin 16
To 0V:
IC9 –12,
pin 8
Outputs
a b c d e f g
13 12 11 10 9 15 14
a b c d e f g
COMM
0V
6 2 1 7
8 4 2 1
0V
ST
BL
5
4
+V
IC11
4511
LT
3
Outputs
a b c d e f g
13 12 11 10 9 15 14
a b c d e f g
D.P.
COMM

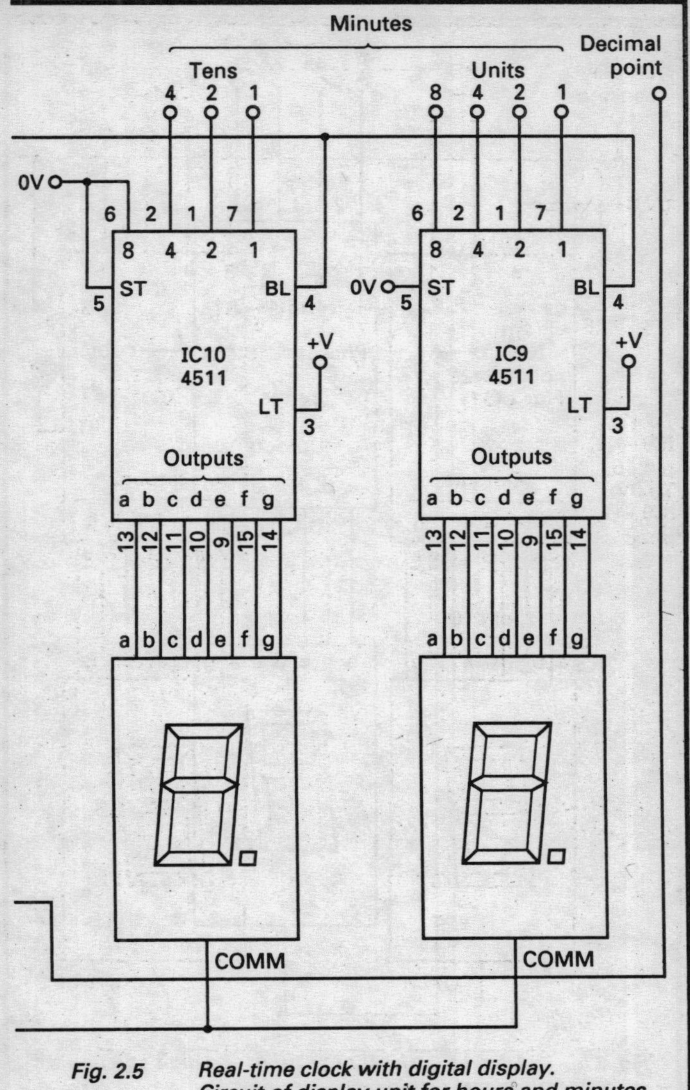

Fig. 2.5 Real-time clock with digital display. Circuit of display unit for hours and minutes.

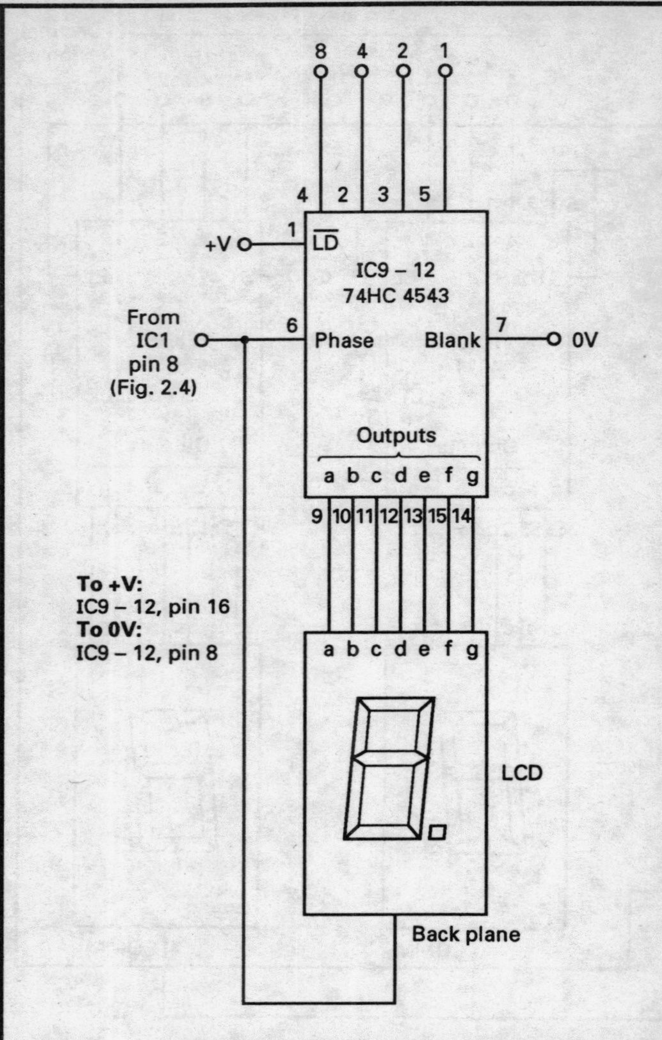

Fig. 2.6 Using a 74HC 4543 to drive one digit of a liquid crystal display.

will result in considerable reduction in the amount of current required, so that battery operation becomes feasible (see page 24). The maximum voltage that this IC can operate at is 6V.

IC3 and IC4 provide for setting the clock to a given time. IC3 is a quadruple 2-line to 1-line demultiplexer. In other words it contains four double-pole switches. The switches are controlled by the SELECT input (pin 1). With this input held low by R6, the four switches are all directed as shown in the figure. The 1Hz signal passes to IC5 and from this to IC6 and then to IC7. The counting chain is continuous. When S4 is closed and the SELECT input made high, the switches are directed to their other poles. Now the dividers are isolated from each other, and each receives a separate input from one of the NOR gates of IC4. These gates are enabled by pressing one of the buttons S1–S3. When a button is pressed, a 2Hz signal passes through the gate to the corresponding divider. The divider is incremented twice each second, allowing its count to be set as required. The figure shows setting for hours, minutes and seconds. Seconds setting is not required for the basic clock, so S3 and R5 are omitted, with pin 1 of IC4 being connected directly to 0V.

When an LED display is used, there are four 4511 decoders to convert the binary codes from the divider chain into outputs suitable for driving the 7-segment LED arrys. Note that there are *no resistors* between the decoders and the LEDs. This is because the project uses *low-current* displays that can be driven directly. Even so, there is a risk of overloading the ICs and this is avoided by making use of the blanking input. A low input to pin 4 of the ICs causes the display to be turned off. This input is connected to the AND gate IC8c (see Figure 2.4). The gate receives inputs from the 7th and 8th stages of the counter. These run through the cycle 00, 01, 10, 11, at the rate of 64 times per second. Only when *both* stages are high (11) is the gate output high and the display turned on. Thus the display is on for only one quarter of the time, reducing power dissipation sufficiently. The repetition rate is so fast that the display shows no flickering and the LEDs appear to be brightly lit.

The 1Hz signal from IC2 is used to flash one of the decimal points to indicate seconds.

Construction: The basic clock requires a circuit board measuring about 10cm × 16cm. There is room on a board of this size for the alarm circuits too. Elaborate wiring can be reduced by drafting the board as a PCB. On the other hand, the use of stripboard makes it easier to modify the wiring later if further additions and expansions are envisaged. You may decide that the display is best built as a separate unit; this makes it easier to interpose modules such as the memory unit at a later stage. A 25-pin D-connector is suitable in most applications.

The power requirements for the simple clock are 3V to 6V DC, which need not be closely regulated. At 6V, the circuit requires about 50mA to drive it (including the alarm registers described in the next section) plus 70mA for each LED digit. This gives a total of about 320mA for a 4-digit (hours/minutes) display. This is best provided by a mains PSU rated at 600mA and 6V DC, as this will allow scope for expansion. Power requirements can be reduced by inserting series resistors between the output of IC9–12 and the display units (also see page 136). An LCD display takes so little current that the clock circuit and display together require only 50mA. A 300mA PSU provides ample current for this as well as for various other additions which may be connected later.

The circuit can also be powered by batteries at 3V, 4.5V or 6V. At 3V, only about 70mA is required but, as the batteries become drained, the voltage eventually falls below 3V and the circuit ceases to operate properly. At 4.5V the circuit requires 30mA plus 180mA for a 4-digit display. The display is not as bright as when the supply is 6V, but is adequate for most purposes. Using an LCD reduces power consumption to 30mA so that three alkaline D cells will last over a fortnight. An alternative is to use an LED display and to install a switch so that the blanking inputs of IC9–12 can be connected to 0V instead of to IC8, pin 10. This allows the display to be turned off when not required.

When planning the PCB, or when laying out the stripboard, it is essential to allow space for decoupling capacitors connected between the +V and 0V lines. There must be an electrolytic capacitor (about 22μF) where the power lines enter the board. There should also be another (about 470μF) where the power lines enter the display area of the board (or on a separate display board). Disc ceramic capacitors (about 22nF) should be scattered around the board at the rate of about 1 capacitor for every 5 ICs (2 or 3 for the basic clock).

Begin with the crystal oscillator and IC1; solder the components of the oscillator as close together as possible so as to avoid capacitative effects. According to several references C2 should be a 5–65pF trimmer capacitor, but trimming makes little difference to the operation, and a fixed value capacitor works well. The circuit can be checked by using an oscilloscope, or connect an LED and 330Ω resistor in series between pin 3 and the 0V lines. The LED flashes at 2Hz. Next wire up the divide-by-2 stage (IC2) and check its output.

Before the dividers can be installed, wire in IC3 and IC4. At this stage it is not necessary to wire in the push-buttons S1–S3 or the switch S4, because the pull-down resistors hold the inputs low, as required for normal time-keeping.

Connect and check the divider ICs one at a time, starting with IC5. It is possible to check its operation with an LED wired to each output (see Figure 3.17), but it is easier to assemble two of the display digits (IC9 and IC10 with displays) and use these to give a proper readout from the two dividers of the IC being tested. Note that the 7-segment display must be of the common *cathode* type. A common *anode* display does not work in this circuit. Remember to connect the display blanking line before attempting to test the circuit.

If the divider apparently fails to count correctly, check all connections between the divider and the decoder, and between the decoder and the LED display, as it is very easy to interchange two wires accidentally, and even a single bad solder joint can make the display behave very erratically. One problem that may arise at this stage is that inputs to a CMOS IC must be connected to *something.* Having assembled IC5 with IC8a, the other three gates of IC8 are unused at this stage. If the inputs of the unused gates are not connected, the IC may not behave correctly. If so, either assemble the complete chain before testing the dividers individually, or temporarily connect the unused inputs of IC8 to 0V or the positive supply.

Checking the minutes and hours dividers could be a lengthy process but time is saved by using a faster output from IC1. When checking minutes, disconnect pin 3 of IC1 and take the output from pin 14 (stage 8) instead. This runs 64 times faster than pin 3, so the minutes divider then runs at just over 1 count per second. Similarly, when checking the hours divider, use the output from IC1 pin 7 (stage 4). This runs at 1024 times the rate of pin 3, giving about 3 counts per second.

The setting circuits are checked by closing S4. A 2Hz signal is found at pins 4, 7 and 12 whenever one of the corresponding buttons S1–S3 is pressed. At the same time, the display of the corresponding counter is advanced twice each second. Note that there is no carry-over from seconds to minutes or from minutes to hours.

The circuit (and power supply, if not of the type that plugs into the mains socket) is housed in a suitable plastic enclosure with an aperture cut for the display. S1–S4 are mounted on the top or front panel of the housing. The appearance of the display can be enhanced and made more contrasty under bright ambient lighting if a non-reflective filter of the same colour as the LEDs is mounted in front of the display.

Expansions

(a) Alarm output

This greatly increases the usefulness of the basic clock described above, but the basic clock operates perfectly well as a time-keeper without the alarm function so this addition can be left until later, if preferred. The circuit shown in Figure 2.7 is for an alarm which is settable for hours and minutes, but not for seconds.

How it works: The alarm register, which holds the time at which the alarm signal is to be generated, consists of two dividers IC14 and IC15. These are of the same type as used in the divider chain of the clock. IC14 is wired so as to register minutes from 00 to 59; IC15 registers hours from 00 to 23. The other major addition is a set of multiplexers IC17–20. These connect the display unit either to the clock registers IC6–7 or to the alarm registers IC14–15. In this circuit we use 40257 multiplexers instead of 40157s as in the basic clock. The 40257 multiplexers have 3-state outputs so are suitable for connecting to a data bus should the clock be modified as a time recorder (page 33).

The operation of the clock is controlled by a 3-pole 4-position rotary switch which replaces the single-pole switch S4 of Figure 2.4:

Position 1: the clock operates in exactly the same way as in Figure 2.4 except that the signals from IC6–7 are routed to the display through the multiplexers IC17–20. The alarm does not sound in this position.

Position 2: as position 1 except that the alarm sounds when the pre-set time is reached.

Position 3: this is the equivalent of closing S4 of Figure 2.4. Pressing S1 and S2 sets the hours and minutes of the clock.

Position 4: the multiplexers now connect the display to the outputs of the alarm registers. Pressing S1 and S2 sets the hours and minutes of the alarm registers, as the high input on one terminal of gates IC13a and IC13d allows the 2Hz signals to pass from IC4.

When the alarm has been set to a given time and S4 returned to position 2, the outputs of IC6–7 are compared bit-by-bit with the outputs of IC14–15. This is done with a pair of digital comparators IC21–22, as shown in Figure 2.8. Each of these has a $\overline{P=Q}$ output, which is normally high. When the input from the clock (P) exactly matches the input from the corresponding alarm register (Q), this output goes low. When the time on the clock reaches the time set on the alarm registers, both $\overline{P=Q}$ outputs go low, and the output of IC4c goes high. Provided that S4 is set to position 2, the output of IC16c also goes high. This high output is used to activate the alarm sounder circuit.

Many designs of alarm sounder circuit are possible. Indeed, any other device such as a lamp, a motor or a relay, which can be activated by a logic high can be triggered. Figure 2.9 shows sounder circuits. Figure 2.9a in conjunction with Figure 2.9c

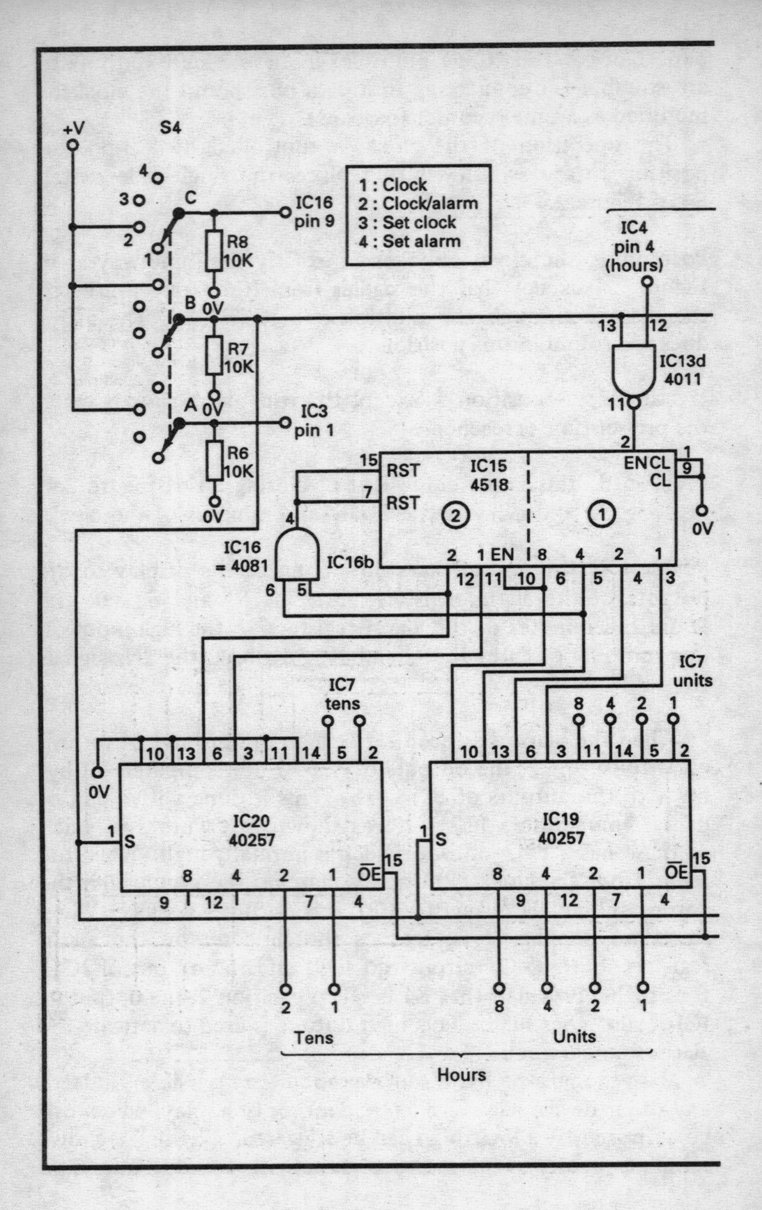
+V
S4
1 : Clock
2 : Clock/alarm
3 : Set clock
4 : Set alarm
IC16
pin 9
R8
10K
0V
R7
10K
R6
10K
IC3
pin 1
IC4
pin 4
(hours)
IC13d
4011
IC15
4518
RST
RST
EN
CL
IC16
= 4081
IC16b
IC7
tens
IC7
units
IC20
40257
IC19
40257
S
OE
Tens
Units
Hours

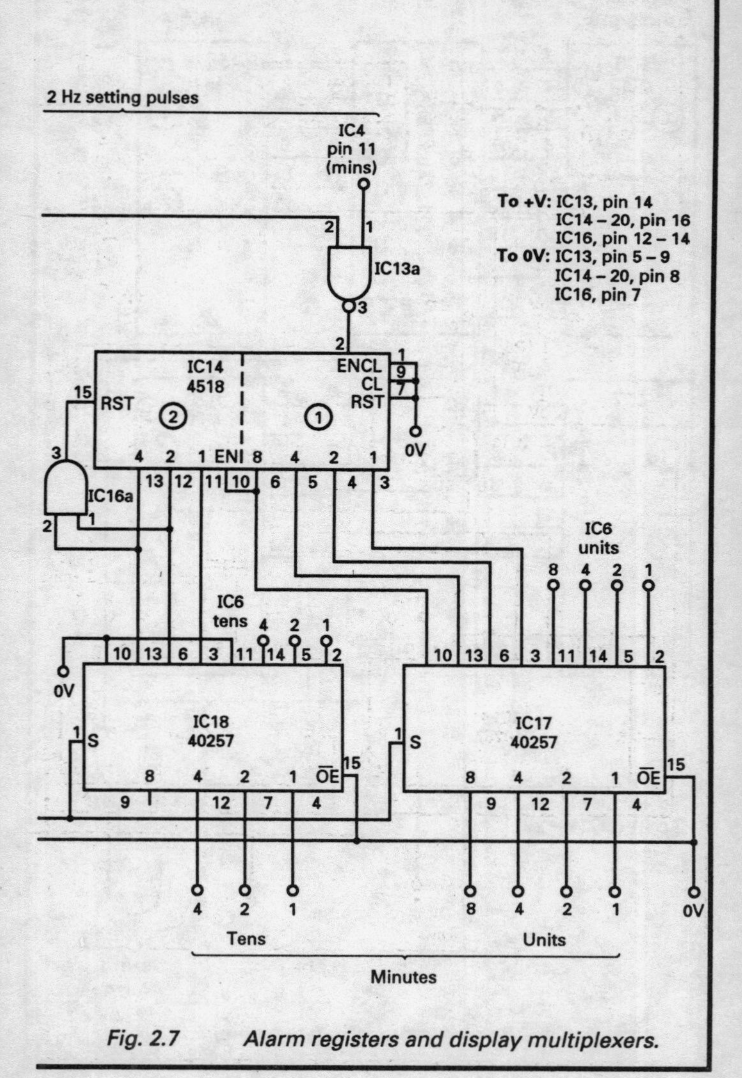

Fig. 2.7 Alarm registers and display multiplexers.

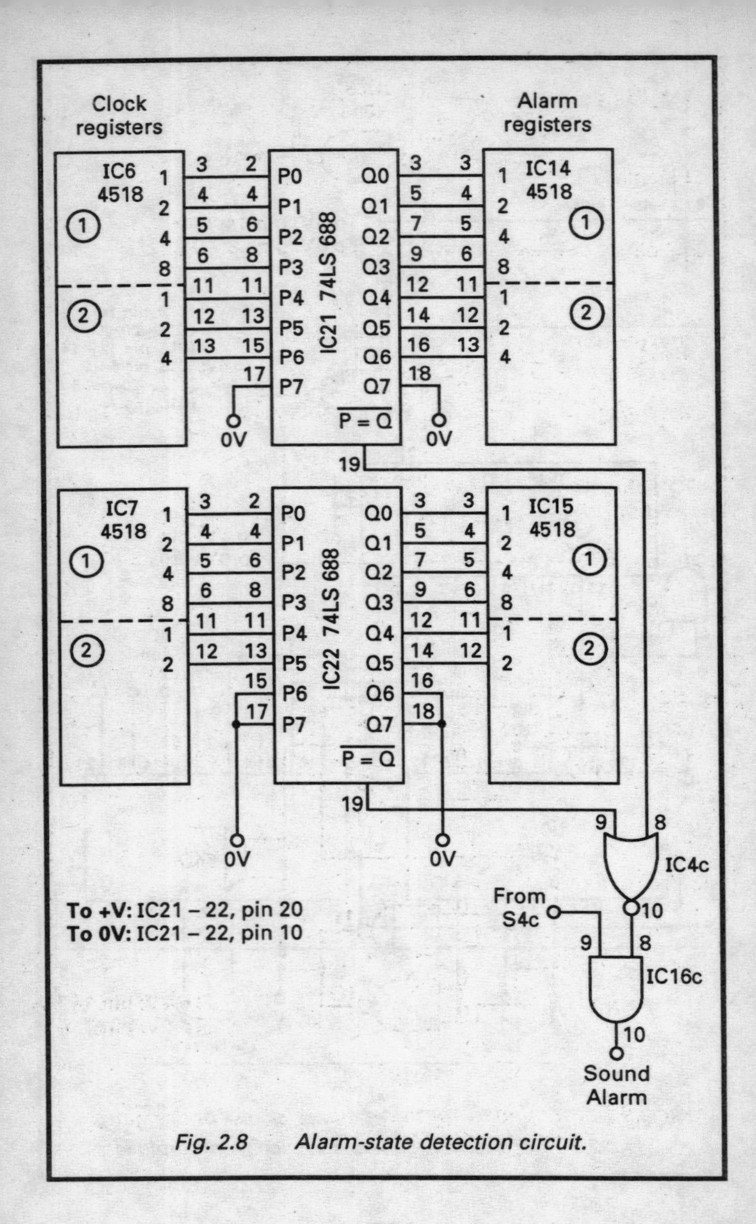

Fig. 2.8 Alarm-state detection circuit.

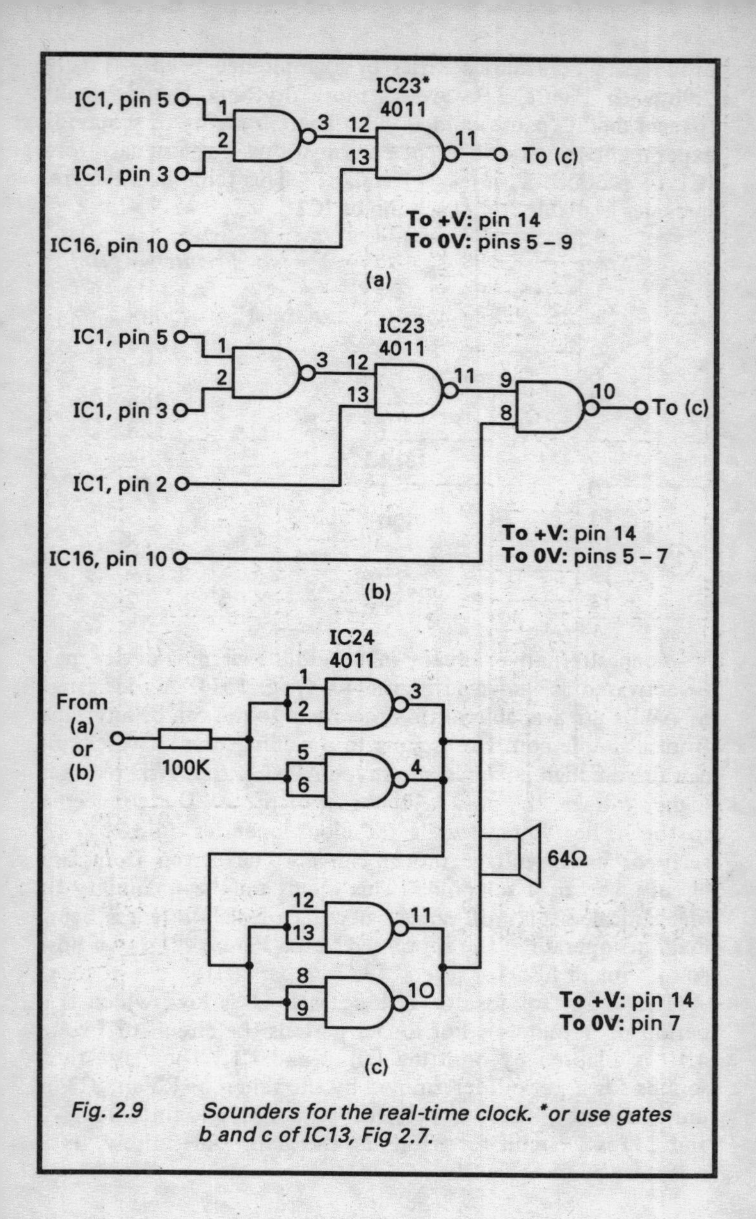

Fig. 2.9 *Sounders for the real-time clock. *or use gates b and c of IC13, Fig 2.7.*

produces a continuous series of high-pitched beeps. Figure 2.9b with Figure 2.9c gives a more rhythmic sound: de-dit (pause) de-dit (pause) and so on. There is plenty of scope for experimenting with different combinations of the signals from IC1 to produce a variety of sounds. This table lists the frequencies available from each pin of IC1:

Stage	*Pin*	*Frequency (Hz)*
4	7	2048
5	5	1024
6	4	512
7	6	256
8	14	128
9	13	64
10	15	32
11	Not available	
12	1	8
13	2	4
14	3	2

As an alternative, a ready-made audible warning device may be activated as shown in Figure 4.6 (page 151). A wide range of AWDs are available so that the alarm sound can be anything from a simple continuous tone to a wailing siren. This circuit can drive a high-powered siren-type AWD; if the AWD requires higher voltage, the positive terminal of the AWD is connected to the higher voltage while the clock operates on 3–6V. A relay or a low-voltage motor can also be driven from this circuit, as can a solenoid. This opens up the possibility of mechanical display of various degrees of elaborateness being made to operate at the appointed time. Figure 4.7 shows how to turn on an LED (or several LEDs in parallel).

The alarm sounds for as long as $\overline{P=Q}$ is low, which is a period of 1 minute. For longer periods the circuit of Figure 4.10 is adapted by omitting D1–2 and C1. The alarm then sounds for a period determined by the values of R3 and C2 or until the reset button is pressed. Figure 4.11 (omitting D1–2 and C1) is a circuit for triggering the alarm indefinitely, until it is reset by pressing S1.

Construction: There should be room to accommodate the circuit on the same board as the basic clock. There are no real problems in assembling and testing the circuit, except for the large number of connections required. Keep connecting wires as short as possible and preferably use wires of several different colours to avoid confusion. Connections from IC6–7 now go to IC17–20 instead of to the display. Remove S4 from the basic clock and replace it with the rotary switch. Two more 22nF capacitors are required for decoupling the supply lines.

(b) Seconds display

This is easily assembled by adding another pair of 4511 ICs (Fig. 2.5) and a pair of 7-segment displays. The inputs of the ICs are driven from the outputs of IC5 (Fig. 2.4). Wire in the connections to IC4a, including S3 and R5. It is also possible to extend the alarm register and add a third comparator IC, though there are not likely to be many applications in which this would be worth doing. A seconds display is generally of more interest in elapsed timers and there are designs in Chapter 3 which are appropriate to most applications.

(c) Day of week display

This circuit receives a daily pulse from IC8, which increments the counter IC25 (Fig. 2.10). The output stage of this counter differs from that of the dividers used for the clock and alarm registers. In this IC the output is decoded so as to make just one of its 8 outputs high in turn. The remaining outputs are low. The IC is wired so that it resets to zero on the 8th count, repeating the cycle every 7 days. It is then a simple matter to connect an LED to each output to register the day of the week.

The seven LEDs are arranged on the front panel of the clock in a row or perhaps in a circle, with one or more LEDs of a different colour from the rest to indicate weekly religious days or holidays.

(d) Time recorder

This module automatically records the times at which a single or repeated event takes place. It responds to any

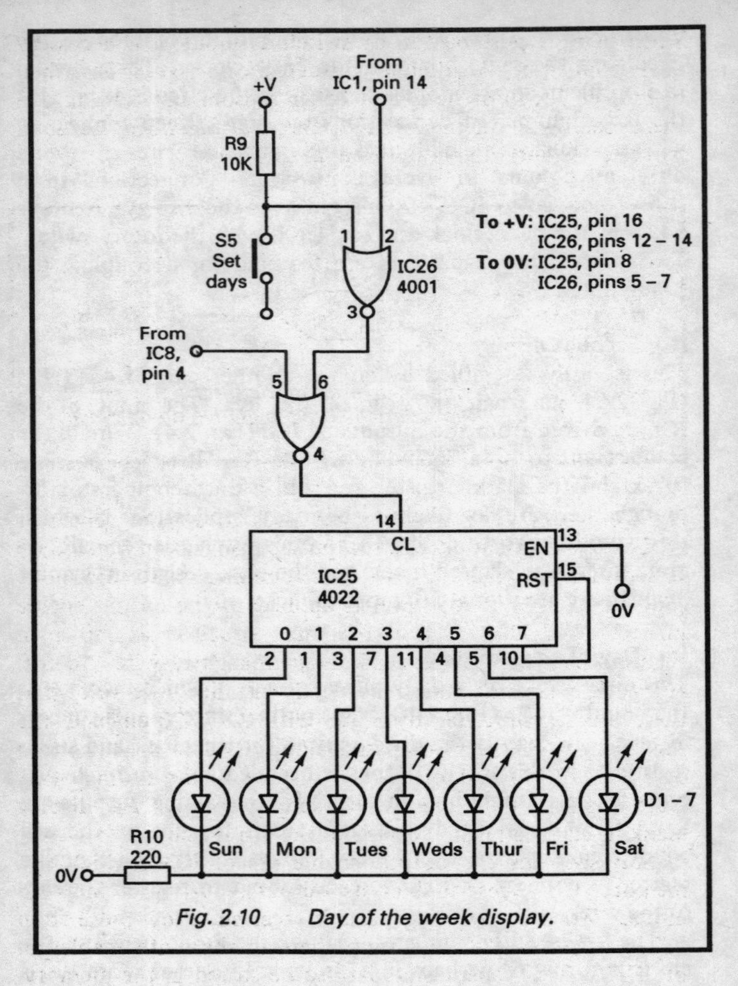

Fig. 2.10 Day of the week display.

triggering event, such as a button being pressed, a switch being closed (e.g. a pressure mat) or (with suitable interface circuits) a light-beam being broken or a sound detected. As shown in Figure 2.11 the circuit responds to a rising logical input at the trigger input. By wiring a logic gate as an inverter (Fig. 2.12), it can also be made to respond to a falling logical input.

When using a push-button or switch as input, it is necessary to de-bounce it. A suitable light-detection trigger is described in Project 11. For details of other sensors and how to use them, see book number BP273, *Practical Electronic Sensors*, by the same author and publisher as this book.

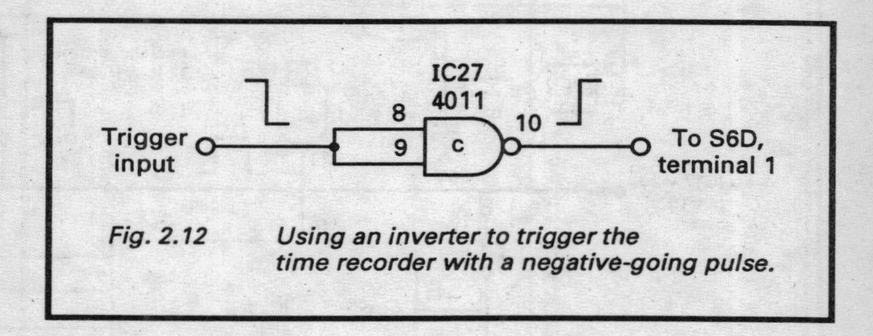

Fig. 2.12 *Using an inverter to trigger the time recorder with a negative-going pulse.*

How it works: The trigger input goes to a pulse generator (IC27a/b) which produces a low pulse lasting about 1ms. Gate IC27d inverts this pulse. When the circuit is in Record mode (S6, position 1), a low level is applied to the output enable pins of IC17–20. This is the same situation as shown in Figure 2.7, where these pins are permanently wired to 0V. However, when the time recorder is installed, the voltage at these pins is controlled by S6A. With IC17–20 enabled, the time output of the clock passes along the data lines (bottom of Figure 2.11) and on to the display in the normal way. Note the 9th data line which simply conveys the display blanking signal straight through to the display circuit.

S6B switches the output enable pin of IC30, which is a memory IC. This disables its outputs, putting it in Read mode. When a triggering pulse is received, a low pulse from IC27a passes to S6C and from there to the write enable pin of IC30. This causes time data to be stored in the memory. The address it is stored at depends upon the logic levels present on address lines A0 to A3. We use only four address lines, allowing 16 addresses (0 to 15) to be accessed. The current address accessed is indicated by the four LEDs which represent the address as a 4-bit binary number from 0000 to 1111. It would be possible to extend the number of

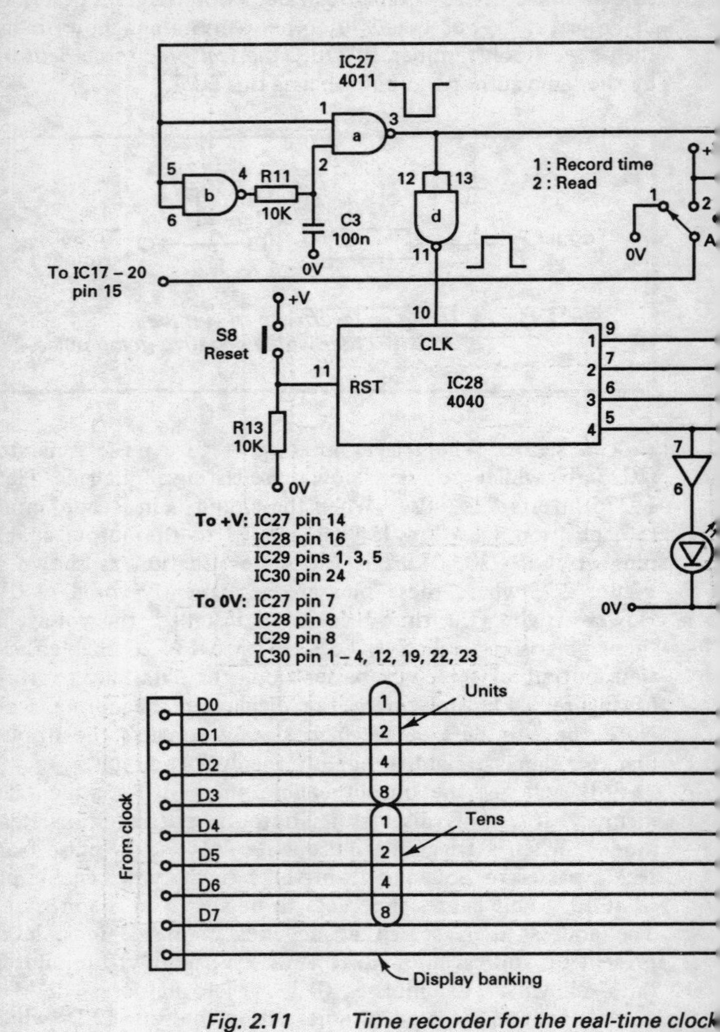

Fig. 2.11 *Time recorder for the real-time clock*

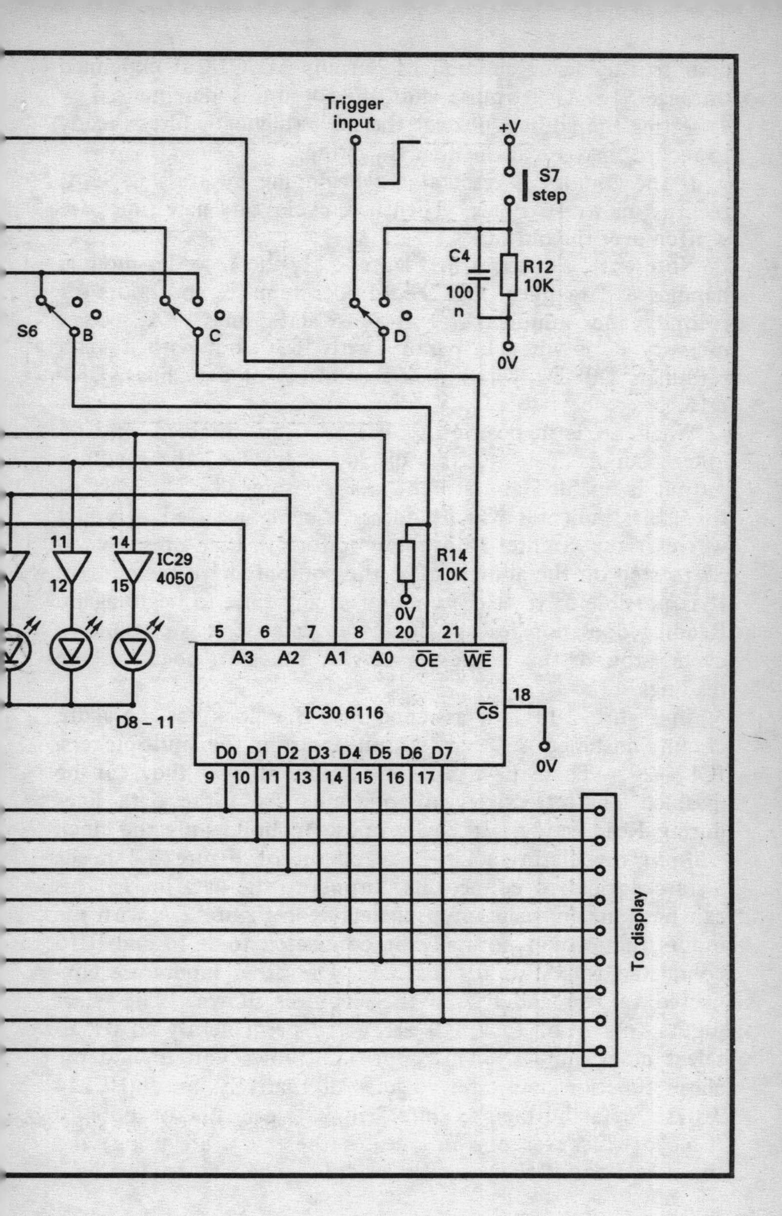

Trigger
input
+V
S7
step
C4
100
n
R12
10K
S6
B
C
D
0V
11
14
IC29
4050
12
15
R14
10K
0V
5
6
7
8
20
21
A3
A2
A1
A0
OE
WE
18
IC30 6116
CS
D8 – 11
D0 D1 D2 D3 D4 D5 D6 D7
0V
9
10
11
13
14
15
16
17
To display

addresses by using subsequent outputs of IC28 as explained on page 51. As the pulse ends, the counter is incremented by 1, setting the address lines at the *next* (higher) address, ready to record the time at the *next* triggering.

If the counter is reset at the beginning by pressing S8, it records up to 16 times. Then it re-cycles and new times are written over the old times.

Note that, as shown in Figure 2.11, the recorder module handles 8 data lines. To record both minutes and hours (or seconds and minutes) requires 16 data lines. A second memory IC is wired in parallel with IC30, but with its data terminals D0–D7 wired to a second set of data lines, D8–D15.

When S6 is in position 2, IC17–20 are disabled, and no longer supply data to the display. Instead, the memory output is enabled and stored data is displayed. The state of the LEDs indicates which address is being accessed. Usually we reset the counter to begin at address 0, then press switch S7 to step on the address after the contents have been noted. It is possible to reset the counter at any time to begin again. Reading does not destroy the stored data, so it is possible to cycle around the addresses several times to re-check the readings.

In Figure 2.11 it is assumed that the clock has the alarm circuits installed so that output is from the multiplexers, IC17–20. These have 3-state outputs so that they can be disabled and effectively disconnected from the data lines during Read mode. If you propose to build only the clock *without* the alarm facility, the circuit of Figure 2.4 needs 3-state devices to connect its outputs to the data lines. This can be done by using multiplexers as in Figure 2.7, with the inputs that would normally be connected to IC14 and IC15 connected to +V or 0V instead. The other inputs are connected to IC6 and IC7 of the clock, as shown. The select inputs (pin 1 of each IC) are wired permanently to 0V to select clock inputs. This approach allows you to add the alarm function at a later stage. Alternatively, use 74HC244 3-state data buffers to interface between the outputs of IC5–7 (whichever one or ones of these you are using) and the data lines of the recorder module. The way to do this is the same as for the data inputs of the data logger circuit (Fig. 2.15).

Summary of control signals

The sequence of control signals is:

Recording:

IC17–20 pin 15 low	Output enabled; time data on data lines
IC30 pin 20 high	Output disabled
IC30 pin 21 high, then a short low pulse	Time written to memory

Reading:

IC17–20 pin 15 high	Output disabled
IC30 pin 20 low	Output enabled
IC30 pin 21 high	Time at current address appears on data lines

Construction: The circuit needs a board about 15cm × 4cm, which can be stripboard or a PCB. If you are making a PCB, consider including the two additional ICs and the connections that are needed to convert this circuit to a data logger, even if you do not assemble this part of the circuit at present. With stripboard there is no problem in making the addition at a later date. S6 is shown in the diagram as a 4-pole 3-way rotary switch. A 2-way switch would be sufficient but it is better to wire in a 3-way switch now, to make it easier to add the data logger feature later. The board requires a 220μF electrolytic capacitor between the +V and 0V lines at the point where the power supply enters the board.

Wire up the pulse generator and counter first, complete with LEDs.

The input must be de-bounced if the counter is not to step on several stages each time. If the trigger is to be a switch or push-button, wire it in the same way as S7, with a capacitor across the resistor. If you prefer, S7 can be used both as triggering input and as a stepping button. Just join together terminals 1 and 2 of S6D.

The LEDs go through the binary sequence step by step each time the input button is pressed. Pressing S8 resets the count to 0000 (all LEDs out). If there is trouble with erratic counting, check all connections carefully. It may help to wire a 22nF decoupling capacitor between the power lines at a point close to the counter.

On the clock board, disconnect pin 15 of IC17–20 from 0V. The point marked 0V at the bottom right of Figure 2.7 is now to be connected to the selector of S6A, Figure 2.11. For neatness and convenience, make this connection through the same plug as is used for the data lines. We also need to implement the full number of data lines from IC17–IC20 instead of just those which were sufficient for displaying time. If you are recording time in minutes, for example, run a line from IC18 pin 9 (Fig. 2.7) to the output plug. On the display board, the corresponding input is now to be wired to the input plug or socket, instead of to 0V (in this example, IC10, pin 6). The same applies to other previously unimplemented lines such as those from IC20, pins 9 and 12. Similarly, if your clock does not have the alarm function and you are using 74HC244 ICs to interface between the clock registers and this module, you will need to run a data line from each output terminal.

When the circuit is completed, check it by plugging in the clock and the display and making the necessary power connections. Use a push-button (e.g. S7) to provide input. Switch S4 to Set Clock mode. Switch S6 to Record mode. Press the Set Minutes button S2 (or other button if you are recording other time periods) and watch the display count correctly. Press S8 to reset the counter; all LEDs go out. Press S2 for an instant and note the reading on the display. Press the input button; the LED display now shows 1. Press S2 again for an instant to change the reading; note it and press S8 again. Proceed in this way until different times are stored at each of the 16 addresses. Now set S6 to position 2, Read mode. Reset the counter and then step through the addresses, using S7. The readings on the display should be identical with those noted while recording.

(e) Periodic trigger

This provides an output pulse of defined length at regular intervals. It is used to drive a device such as a lamp, an LED, an AWD or the data logger (see next section).

How it works: The circuit (see Figure 2.13, page 42) derives its input from the timing chain of the main clock (Fig. 2.4). The alarm extension is not required, though this circuit works just as well if the alarm is installed. The point of connection to the timing chain depends on the interval required between successive triggerings:

Connect to	*Triggers every*	*High for*
IC2, pin 1	1s	0.5s
IC5, pin 6	10s	0.2s
IC8, pin 3	1min	*
IC6, pin 6	10min	12s
IC8, pin 11	1h	*
IC7, pin 6	10h	12min
IC8, pin 4	24h	*

* See note on trigger period below

The input is a high-going pulse, occurring at regular intervals. This is inverted by the NOR gate of IC32 and triggers the timer IC31. Its output goes high for a period of time determined by the value of R15 and C5. The time for which it is high is given by $t = 1.1RC$. With the values indicated in Figure 2.13, t equals approximately 5s. Incidentally, if you have a spare NAND gate or INVERT gate on the board, this may be used instead of IC32a.

The points in the table marked * given an extremely short high pulse as the IC is reset, so these are ideal for triggering the timer. The other points are high for longer and re-trigger the timer for as long as they are high. This does not make any difference if t is longer than the length of the pulse. If t is to be shorter than the pulse (e.g. less than 12min when the interval is 10 hours), substitute the pulse generator of Figure 2.14 for the single gate of Figure 2.12. This produces a brief

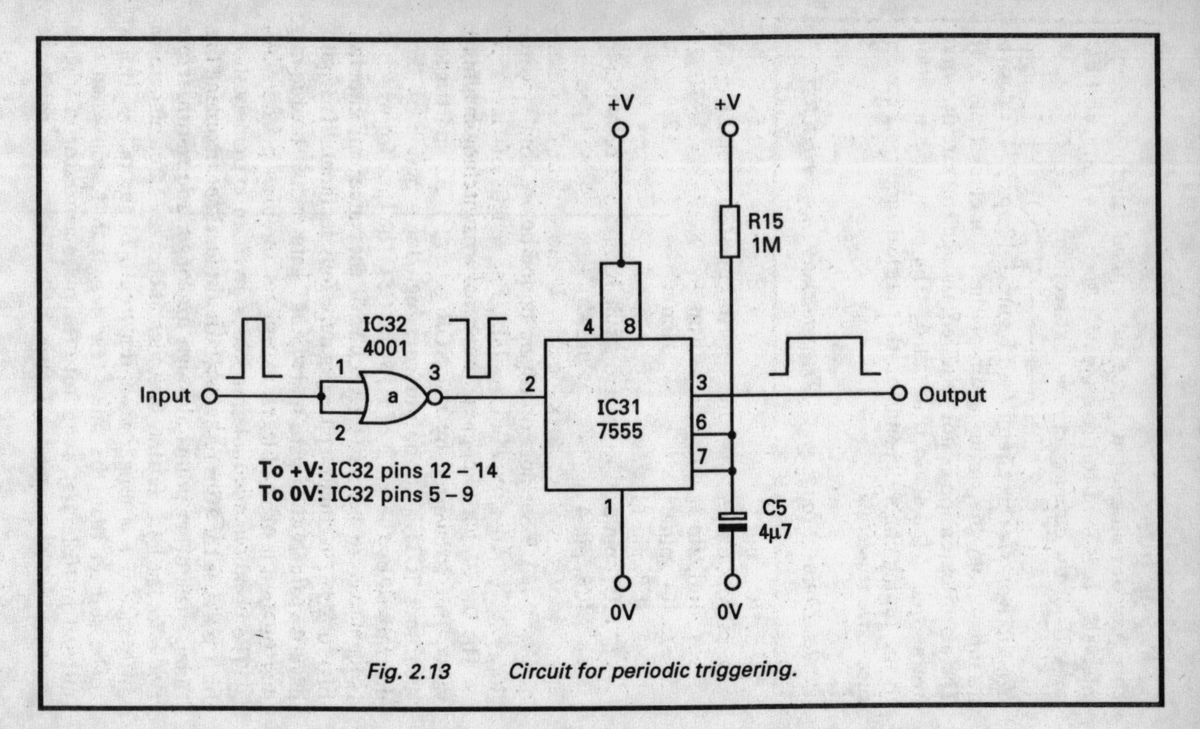

Fig. 2.13 Circuit for periodic triggering.

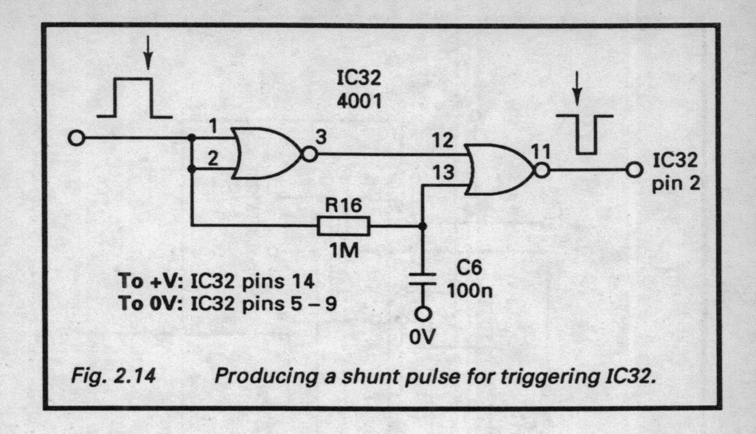

Fig. 2.14 *Producing a shunt pulse for triggering IC32.*

low pulse on a *falling* edge, so it operates at the seconds, minutes or hour count changes from 9, 19, 29, etc., to 10, 20, 30, etc.

Construction: Using only one small IC and one or two additional gates, this circuit can usually be accommodated in a spare corner of the clock board. If more than one of the points listed in the table is to be tapped, use a rotary switch for selecting the required period. The length of time *t* for which the output is high can be varied by switching in a range of resistors in place of R16.

(f) Data logger

This allows the recording of 8 bits of data at regular intervals. It requires the periodic trigger (previous section). The pulse length of this should be short, say 1s. Time is displayed during the operation of the logger, except for the brief period when data is being recorded.

Figure 2.15 shows the way that the time recorder (Fig. 2.11) is extended to include data-logging. The logger therefore includes the ICs, LEDs, switches and other items shown in Figure 2.11, as well as those in Figure 2.15.

How it works: The circuit is capable of recording 8 bits (one byte) of data each time it receives a high pulse from the

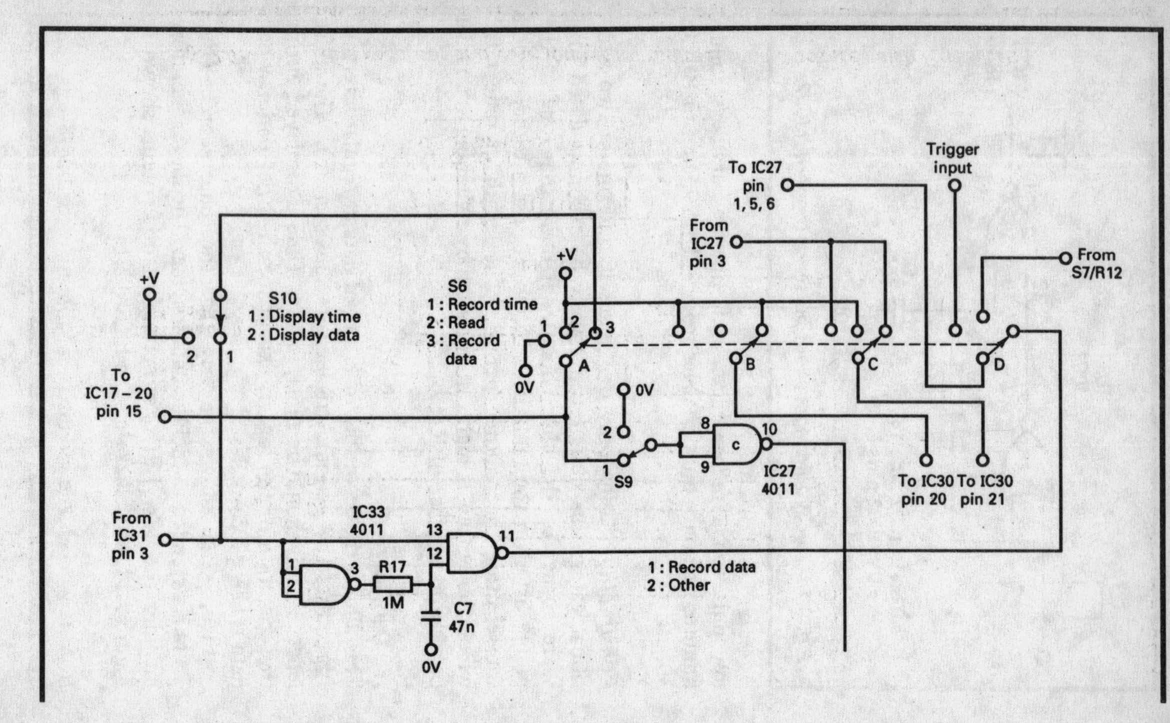
To IC27
pin
1, 5, 6
Trigger
input
From
IC27
pin 3
From
S7/R12
+V
S10
1 : Display time
2 : Display data
+V
S6
1 : Record time
2 : Read
3 : Record
data
1
2
3
A
B
C
D
2
1
0V
To
IC17 – 20
pin 15
0V
2
8
10
c
9
1
S9
IC27
4011
To IC30
pin 20
To IC30
pin 21
From
IC31
pin 3
IC33
4011
13
11
12
1
2
3
R17
1M
C7
47n
0V
1 : Record data
2 : Other

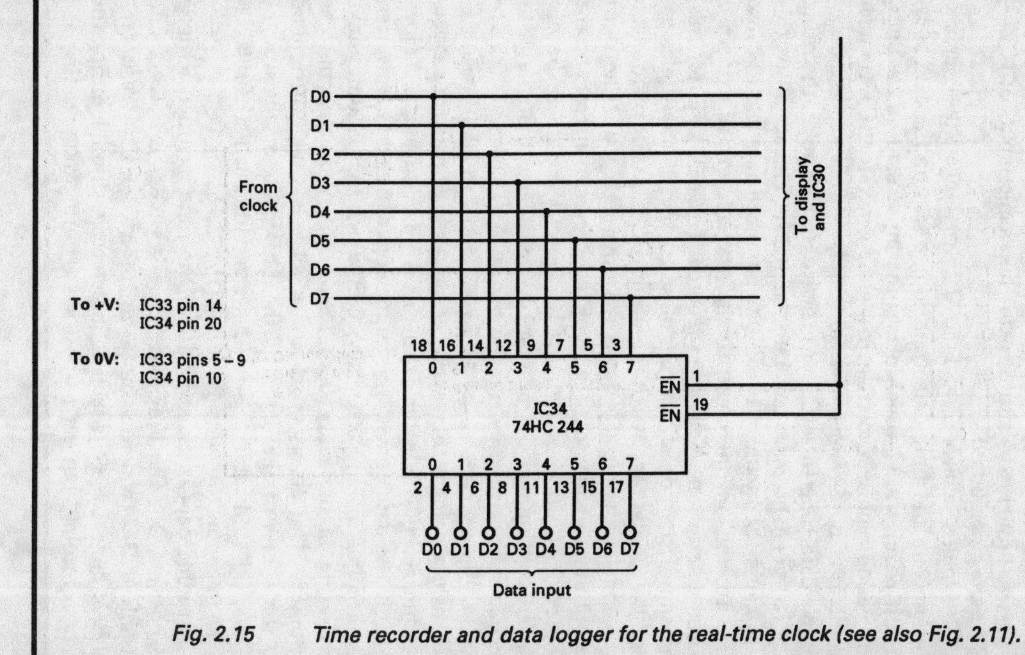

Fig. 2.15 Time recorder and data logger for the real-time clock (see also Fig. 2.11).

periodic trigger of the clock. It receives data from a set of 8 inputs, which are made high or low by external circuitry (perhaps from an analogue-to-digital converter).

For recording data on 16 consecutive occasions, S6 is set to position 3. When a high pulse arrives from the periodic trigger, it passes through S10 and S6A to the enable inputs of IC17–20 on the clock board.

This pulse, which should be 0.2s or longer, disables the mutliplexers and time data is no longer sent on the data lines. Also it enables IC34 which places the input data on the lines. The periodic pulse also triggers a pulse-generator IC33, which produces a short (50ms) low-going pulse. This acts as a delay to give data time to settle. At the end of this pulse, the rising edge triggers the pulse generator of IC27. The action of this is to cause the memory IC IC30 to store the data and to cause IC28 to step on one count to the next address, as explained in the description of the time recorder (page 33). After this, the end of the periodic trigger pulse enables the multiplexers, disables the data input IC; the display shows time once again.

Normally the display shows the time, except for the short period during which data is being recorded and appears on the display. An optional switch S10 allows the data to be displayed continuously. One point to consider is that the 4511 decoders operate only in the range 0–9 (binary 0000 to 1001). Binary codes from 10 to 15 (1010 to 1111) result in the display going blank. With certain types of data (in particular, binary coded digital data) this is no disadvantage. However, if the data comes from an analogue-to-digital converter, for example, or any other device in which the data may take *any* value in the range 0 to 127, a binary display must be installed. This consists of a row of 8 LEDs, which correspond to the 8 bits of the data. If the LED is lit, it indicates '1'; if unlit, it indicates '0'. The wiring for such a display is given in connection with Project 2 (Fig. 2.16).

Reading data is the same as for the time recorder, with S6 in position 2. The only difference is that it is necessary to disable IC34 (which is not present in the time recorder). This is done by S9, which is in set to position 1 during the data recording, but set to position 1 during data reading and time recording or reading.

Summary of control signals:
The sequence of control signals is:

Recording:

IC17–20 pin 15 high	Output disabled – time data removed from data lines
IC34 pins 1/19 low	Input/Output enabled – input data on data lines
IC30 pin 20 high	Output disabled
IC33 pin 11, high, then a 50ms low pulse	The end of this pulse triggers IC27
IC30 pin 21 high, then a short low pulse	Data written to memory
IC34 pins 1/19 high	Intput/Output disabled
IC17–20 pin 15 low	Output enabled – time data restored to data lines

Reading:
As for the time recorder, except that IC34 pins 1/19 are high to disable it.

Construction: If you build Figure 2.11 and then make the additions shown in Figure 2.15, you will have a circuit capable of recording times or input data. If you need only a data recorder (logger) the circuit is slightly simplified by omitting the connections to terminals 1 of S6.

The first stages of building and construction are as described for the time recorder. Then add IC33 and IC34, and wire in the additional gate from IC27. You may have decided that an additional 8-bit display is needed, as in Figure 2.16. Testing proceeds in much the same way as for the time recorder, except that you set up various combinations of high and low levels on the data input terminals and verify that they are correctly recorded and read back.

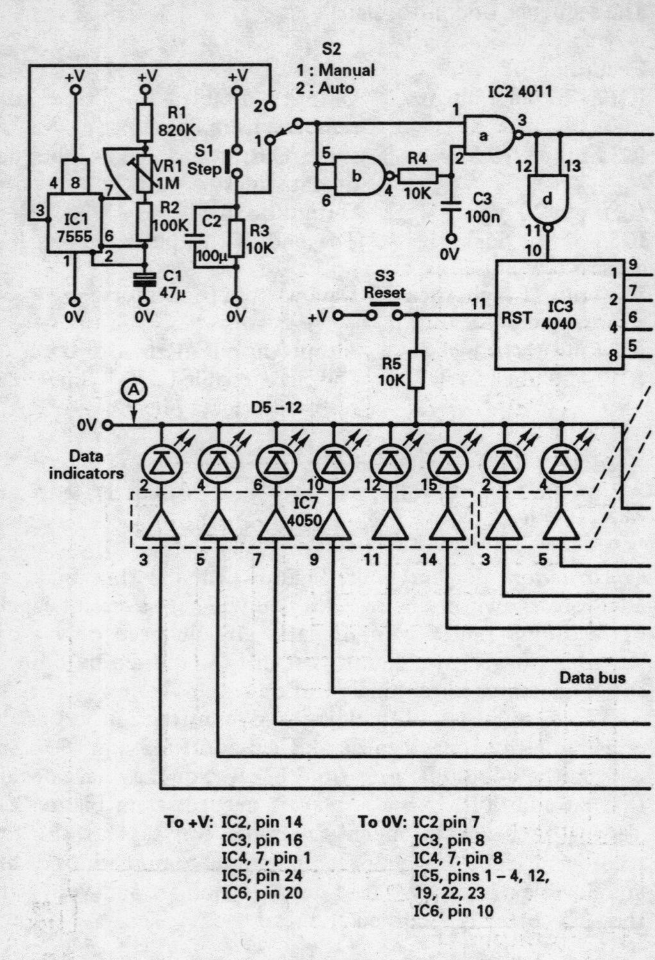

Fig. 2.16 Simple data logger.

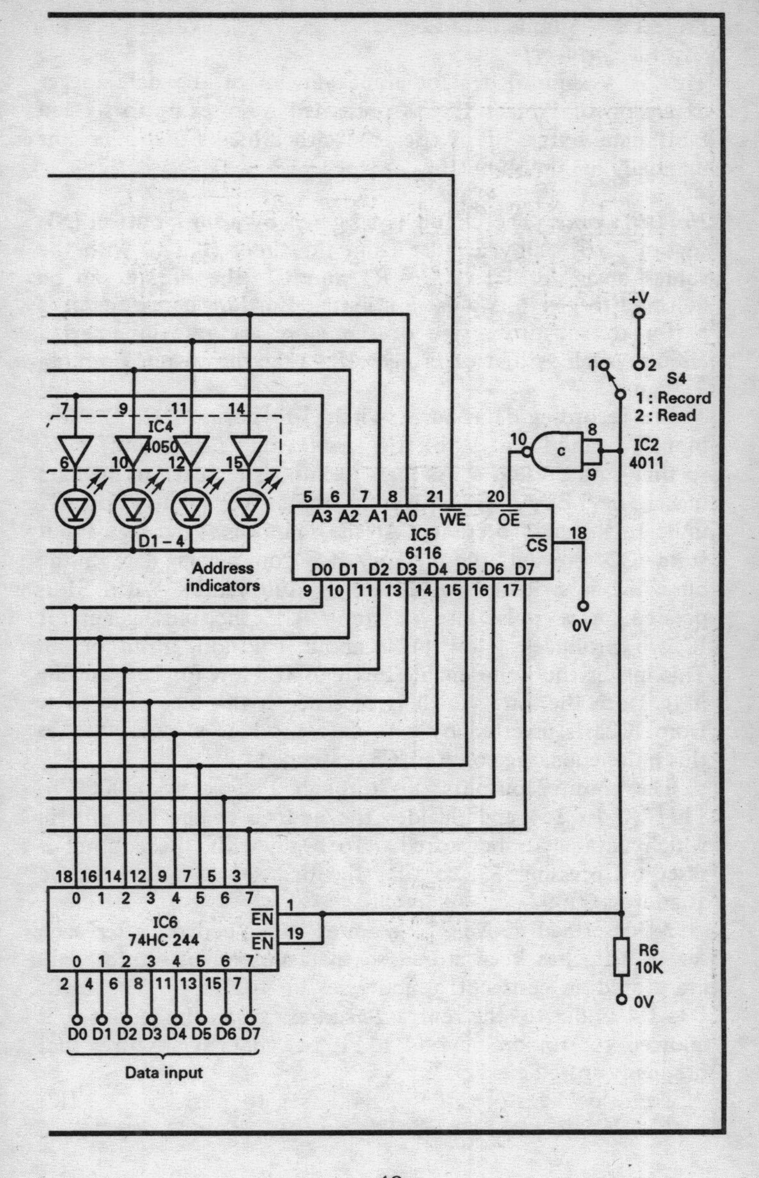

+V
1
2
S4
1 : Record
2 : Read
IC2
4011
10
8
9
c
7
9
11
14
IC4
4050
6
10
12
15
D1 – 4
Address
indicators
5
6
7
8
21
20
A3
A2
A1
A0
WE
OE
IC5
6116
CS
18
D0
D1
D2
D3
D4
D5
D6
D7
9
10
11
13
14
15
16
17
0V
18
16
14
12
9
7
5
3
0 1 2 3 4 5 6 7
IC6
74HC 244
EN
EN
1
19
0 1 2 3 4 5 6 7
2
4
6
8
11
13
15
7
D0 D1 D2 D3 D4 D5 D6 D7
Data input
R6
10K
0V

Project 2 – Simple Data Logger
(Average project)
This is a simplified stand-alone version of the data logger extension of Project 1. As presented it stores up to sixteen 8-bit data bytes. It is triggered either by its own clock or manually by a push-button.

How it works: The circuit is triggered by a push-button (S1, Figure 2.16) or by a pulse from the timer (IC1). With the values given for R1, R2, VR1 and C1, the timing can be adjusted to give one pulse a minute. For longer periods, it is better to substitute one of the more accurate long-period circuits, such as that of Project 18. Take the output from pin 3, Figure 3.27.

For recording data, S4 is switched to position 1. The low input to pins 1 and 19 of IC6 enables the tri-state buffer IC, so that data present at its input terminals appears on the data bus. The LEDs 5–12, driven by the buffers of IC4 and IC7 indicate the data present. At the same time, the high input from IC2c prevents the memory IC5 from placing data on the bus. S2 is switched to Manual or Automatic. When S1 is pressed or a pulse arrives from IC1, the pulse-generator IC2a/b produces a low pulse about 1ms long from pin 3. This makes the write enable input of IC5 low for 1ms causing it to store the data which is present on the bus. The pulse from IC2a is inverted by gate d to produce a high pulse; as this pulse ends, the counter IC3 is stepped on.

The counter outputs run through a cycle from 0000 to 1111 (0 to 15) and decides the address in the memory in which data is to be stored. To begin with, the counter is reset by pressing S3, so that the first set of data is stored at address 0000.

As described above, the counter is stepped on *after* each set of data has been stored so that subsequent sets of data are stored in consecutive addresses up to 1111. The LEDs D1–D4 indicate the current address. If the counter is allowed to run on beyond 1111, new data over-writes that originally stored.

To read the stored data, S4 is set to position 2. This enables IC5 to place stored data on the bus, and prevents IC6 from putting data on the bus. Also S2 is set to position 1, for stepping on the address. Press S3 to reset the counter. The LEDs D5–D12 now display the data stored at address 0000. Each time S1 is pressed, the address is incremented and the stored data is displayed.

The circuit can be extended in two ways. The number of bits stored may be increased (to 16, for example) by wiring a second memory IC in parallel with IC5, and a second buffer IC in parallel with IC6. These two additional ICs are connected to a new set of data lines D8 to D15. Another 8 buffer gates are required together with 8 more LEDs. The other extension is to increase the number of addresses. This is more easily done because all that is needed to double the addresses to 32 is an extra address line from IC3, pin 3 to IC5, pin 4, with a buffer and LED to indicate its state. For even more addresses make the following connections:

No. of addresses	*IC3 pin*	*IC5 pin*
64	3	3
126	2	2
256	4	1
512	13	23

The limitation on both extensions is the difficulty of reading binary numbers as the number of digits increases. Converting binary to a digital output is possible, but complicated, and the circuit would no longer be a *simple* data logger.

Construction: The circuit requires a board about 7cm × 16cm, and a 6V power supply. Total power requirement is just under 50mA for the circuit, plus about 4mA for each LED (actually 8mA each, but any given LED is on for only half the time). Since the device is likely to be used for relatively short periods, a 6V battery is a possibility. To conserve power when operating for longer periods, insert a switch at point A, so that the cathodes of the LEDs may be disconnected from the 0V line, turning the display off when not required. Alternatively, use a series resistor as in Figure 3.26.

The circuit requires decoupling: a 470μF electrolytic capacitor at the point where the power lines enter the board, and two or three 22nF ceramic plate capacitors between the power lines at convenient points, especially near to the counter and memory power pins.

Build the timer circuit IC1 and push-button circuit first and check their output levels and the timing of IC1, using a voltmeter. If you require other timing periods, substitute resistors of different values. It is also possible to switch in a range of resistors in place of VR1 and R2 to allow different time periods to be selected. Next build the pulse generator; its output is normally high. It gives a low pulse when triggered; this can be detected with an oscilloscope but otherwise wait until IC3 has been added. Then pressing S2 repeatedly steps on the counter. Complete the assembly of the circuit. It should then behave as described above. There are many points in the circuit where a dry joint or an incorrect connection can upset the recording, storing or the displaying of data, so check all soldering carefully. If you are using stripboard, it is very helpful to use wires of 8 different colours for the data lines.

Project 3 – Striking Clock

(Average project)

The purpose of having a bell to strike the hour is to make the time known to everyone within earshot of the clock, even though they may not be near enough to see the dial. For centuries, clocks on churches and public buildings (for example, the Houses of Parliament) have been equipped with a striking mechanism. This was a great convenience, for it is only in comparatively recent times that the majority of people have had personal and portable timepieces such as watches. This project may not sound like Big Ben, but its function is the same, to indicate the hour by the number of strikes.

The project consists of 3 parts. Part 1 is the clock and sensor. The clock has hands and a dial. Purchase a basic quartz clock module for a few pounds or adapt an existing dial clock for this purpose. The sensor unit is attached to the clock so that it detects the position of the second and

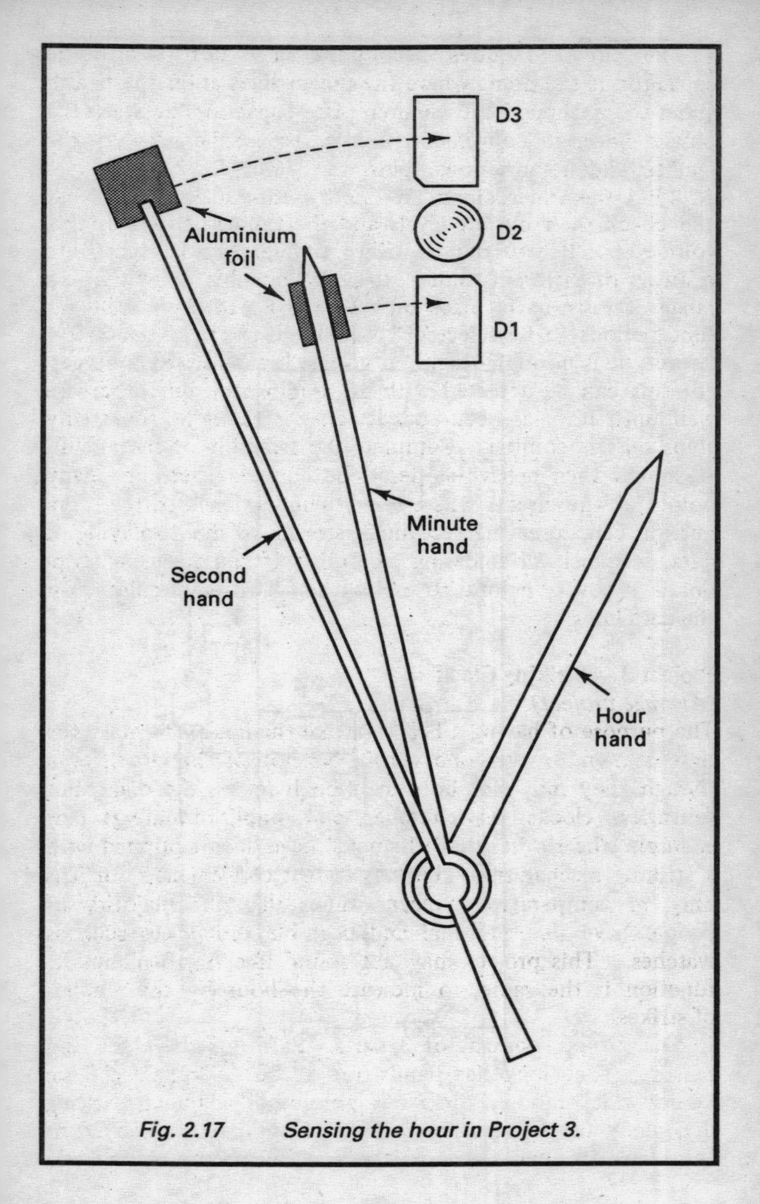

Fig. 2.17 Sensing the hour in Project 3.

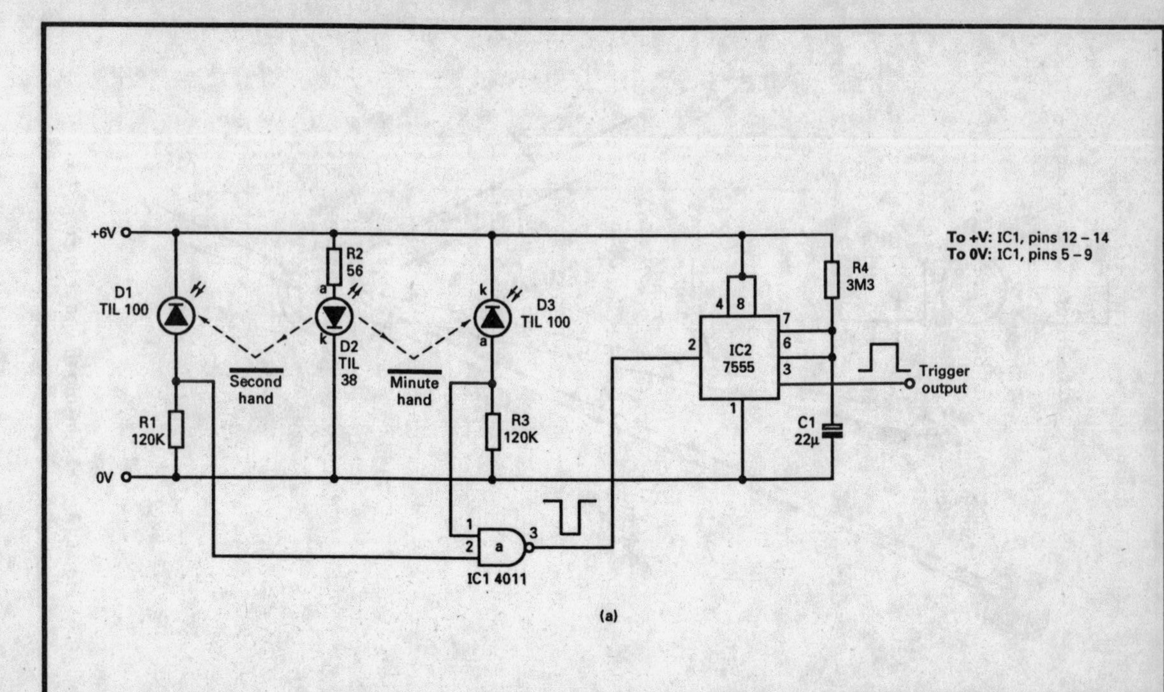

+6V
D1
TIL 100
R2
56
a
k
D2
TIL
38
k
D3
TIL 100
a
Second
hand
Minute
hand
R1
120K
R3
120K
0V
1
2
a
3
IC1 4011
4
8
7
6
2
IC2
7555
3
1
R4
3M3
C1
22µ
Trigger
output
To +V: IC1, pins 12 – 14
To 0V: IC1, pins 5 – 9

(a)

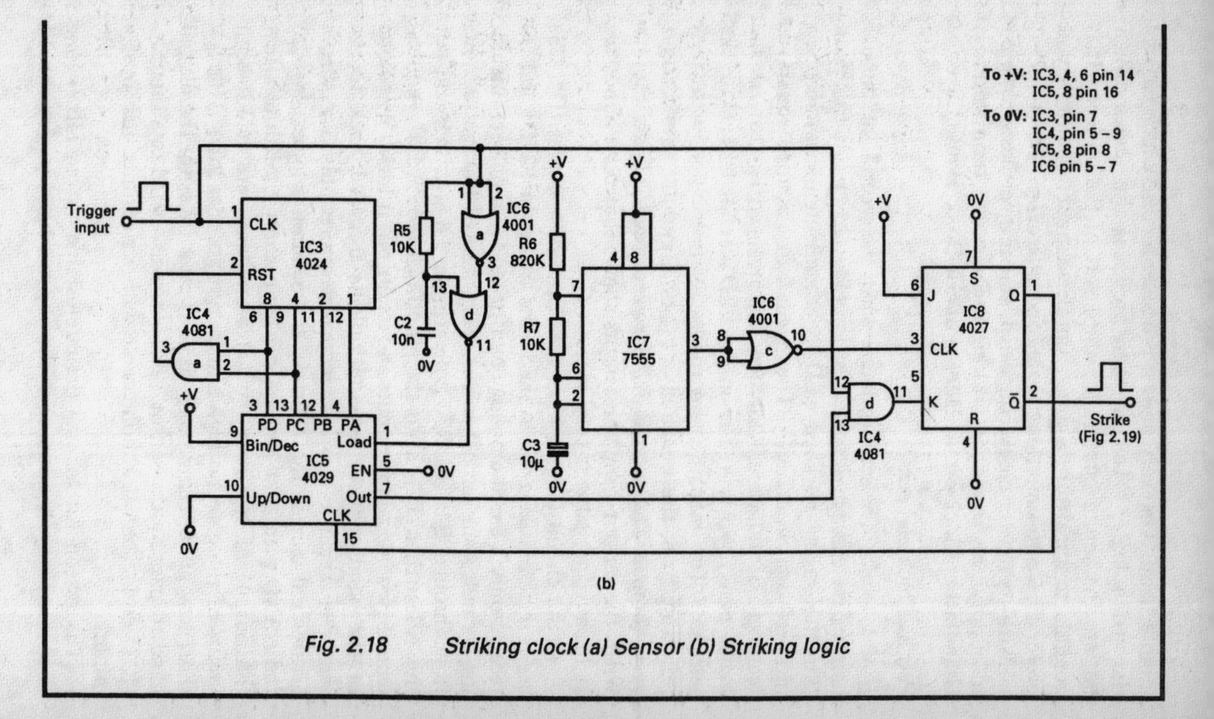

Fig. 2.18 Striking clock (a) Sensor (b) Striking logic

minute hand. On every hour it produces a pulse which triggers the strike logic. This in turn produces the pulses which initiate the sound circuit, the third part of the project. It is possible to substitute a much simpler sounder circuit if you prefer a beep to something more sonorous.

With its master clock concealed, this project has been used to supply the sound of striking for a model (non-working) Grandfather Clock on the landing of our Dolls' House.

Part 1: Clock and sensor

How it works: The sensors detect when the second and minute hands pass the 12 o'clock position (Fig. 2.17). At this position there is an infra-red LED (light-emitting diode) and two infra-red sensor diodes. The hands carry a small square or rectangle of aluminium kitchen foil arranged so that, as the hands pass 12, infra-red from the LED is reflected back to the sensors. The minute hand moves relatively slowly, so it is reflecting back the infra-red for 2 or 3 minutes round about every hour. The second hand sweeps rapidly past the 12. When the output from the sensors shows that *both* hands are at 12, a trigger pulse is produced.

In the circuit (Fig. 2.18a), the two sensor diodes (D1, D3) are reverse biassed. When the hands are not at 12, D1 and D3 receive only a small amount of infra-red from objects (including incandescent lamps) in the room. Small leakage currents flow through R1 and R3, generating a p.d. across them, but this is less than 3V. Thus the NAND gate receives the equivalent of two logical low inputs and its output is high. When one of the hands passes, the foil reflects infra-red back to the sensor. Leakage current increases appreciably, causing a greater p.d. across the resistor, and sending a logical high to the NAND gate. But one logical high is not enough to affect the output of the gate. When *both* hands are at 12, both inputs of the gate are high and its output goes low. This is a short low pulse, lasting only as long as it takes for the second hand to pass by the sensor. The low pulse is fed to a timer IC (IC2) connected as a monostable with a period of just over a minute.

The reason for making the monostable output rather long is that it may happen that the second hand passes the 12 *twice* while the minute hand is there, which would give two trigger pulses each hour. This is particularly likely to happen with certain clocks in which the second hand flicks ahead very vigorously at each 'tick', then bounces slightly back again. Two or more pulses from the NAND gate during the period of 1 minute do not produce another trigger pulse from IC2.

Construction: First decide on the clock mechanism that is to be used for this project. Many types of clock are suitable – either electric, electronic or clockwork. For the prototype we used an inexpensive quartz clock module powered by a 1.5V cell. Preferably the clock should have a sweep second hand but, if it has a small second hand elsewhere on the dial, build two separate sensors one for each hand. If possible, there should be room to mount the sensor unit behind the dial plate, with a slot cut in the plate to expose the diodes. The prototype clock has its mechanism in a small plastic case; the cardboard dial plate extends clear of the case, so there is no problem with mounting the sensor unit. If it is not possible to fit the unit behind the dial plate, the sensor unit may be mounted in front of the hands, though this spoils the appearance of the clock to a certain extent.

The circuit (including the strike logic, sound generator and amplifier) requires a power supply of 6V, at about 100mA. This is best provided by a plug-in mains PSU, which need not be regulated. If the clock is an electric one operating on a lower voltage, it is simpler to use a separate cell or battery, just for the clock.

The sensor unit is built on a small scrap of stripboard. By suitably adjusting the lengths of the leads, and bending them if necessary, the three diodes are mounted close together, with the sensitive surfaces of D1 and D3 level with the top of D2. Many versions of the sensor diode have a chamfered corner (as in Figure A.1, page 161) to indicate which terminal wire is the cathode. Note that in Figure 2.18a the central diode (D2) is drawn with the opposite polarity to D1 and D3.

Cut a slit or aperture in the dial plate and secure the board of the sensor unit behind it, perhaps using double-sided self-adhesive pads ('Sticky fixers'). The positioning and size of the foil squares is important. They should come to be partly in front of the LED and partly in front of the appropriate sensor diode as the hand passes 12. So that they each affect only one sensor, it may be necessary to shorten the minute hand, and also for the foil on the second hand to extend beyond the tip (Fig. 2.17). The foils are fixed to the rear side of each hand using a drop of quick-drying glue (e.g. 'Bostick' or 'Uhu'). Depending on the length of the minute hand, it may be necessary to trim the sides from the foil to reduce the period for which rays are reflected back to the sensor.

When laying out the rest of the circuit, especially if you are making a PCB, note that the unused gates in IC1 are all required for the sounder circuit (Fig. 2.19) should you be including this in your clock. Where Figure 2.18a lists the pin connections to 0V and +V, these connections should be temporary at this stage, except for pin 7 (to 0V) and pin 14 (to +V). Temporary connections allow the sensor circuit to be tested before the sounder circuit is built. If you are using an AWD instead of the sounder circuit, the unused inputs to IC1 should be permanently connected to 0V or +V at this stage.

Complete the circuit and check its action. The inputs to the NAND gate are normally low (less than 2V), but rise almost to 6V when the hand passes. If voltages are always above 3V, reduce the value of R1 and R3 (to 100kΩ, for example). If the levels are always below 3V, increase the resistors. The output of IC2 is normally low (0V) but goes high (6V) for about a minute.

Most of the 65mA taken by this part of the circuit is used by D2. If it is important to conserve current (perhaps in order to make the whole clock battery-powered) try increasing the value of R2. This reduces the amount of infrared produced. Then it may be necessary to increase R1 and R3 to make D1 and D3 more sensitive. This in turn makes the sensors liable to interference by the light from any incandescent lamps that happen to be in the room. This can be avoided if the clock face is shielded from direct illumination.

Part 2: Striking logic

This has to produce one pulse when first triggered, two pulses when next triggered, and so on up to 12 pulses. It returns to 1 pulse at the 13th triggering.

How it works: The counter (IC3, Fig. 2.18b) is incremented by a falling edge, so it is set to a given count at the end of the *previous* pulse. The AND gate of IC4a resets the counter to zero as soon as the output changes to 12; the counter cycles from 0 to 11 repeatedly.

When the trigger input goes high, a pulse generator (IC6) sends a very short high pulse to the LOAD input of IC5. This is another counter, which has the facility of parallel loading; its registers now hold the same count as IC3. This counter differs from IC3 in another way. Where IC3 is a normal 'up' counter, IC5 is programmed to count *down.* This it does when it is clocked by the output of IC8. IC8 is a J-K flip-flop. J is permanently high; when K is also made high, the pulses from the clock (IC7) pass through the flip-flop to output Q and on to IC5. K is high when the trigger input is high AND (gate IC4d) the OUT input of IC5 is also high. The OUT output is high for as long as the count in IC5 is between 0 and 14. Thus when the trigger input goes high the clock pulses cause the count in IC5 to be decremented step by step from its initial value. Each time Q goes low and steps down the counter, $\overline{Q}$ goes high and sends a strike pulse to the sounder circuit (Part 3). Suppose that the counter holds 6 to begin with; the sequence is:

6 5 4 3 2 1 0 15
strike strike strike strike strike strike strike

There are *seven* strikes (one more than the count in IC3 and IC5) at the end of which the count continues down to 15, and the OUT output goes low. This makes K go low and prevents further clock pulses from reaching the flip-flop. IC5 stays in this state, until the next trigger pulse an hour later, so there are no further strikes. The fact that the number of strikes is one more than the number in the counters means that, while the counter cycles from 0 to 11, the number of strikes cycles from 1 to 12.

The input from IC2 must remain high for the whole of the striking period, which is another reason why IC2 must have a long period. After the correct number of strikes has been made, the circuit remains in a steady state. Then, as the

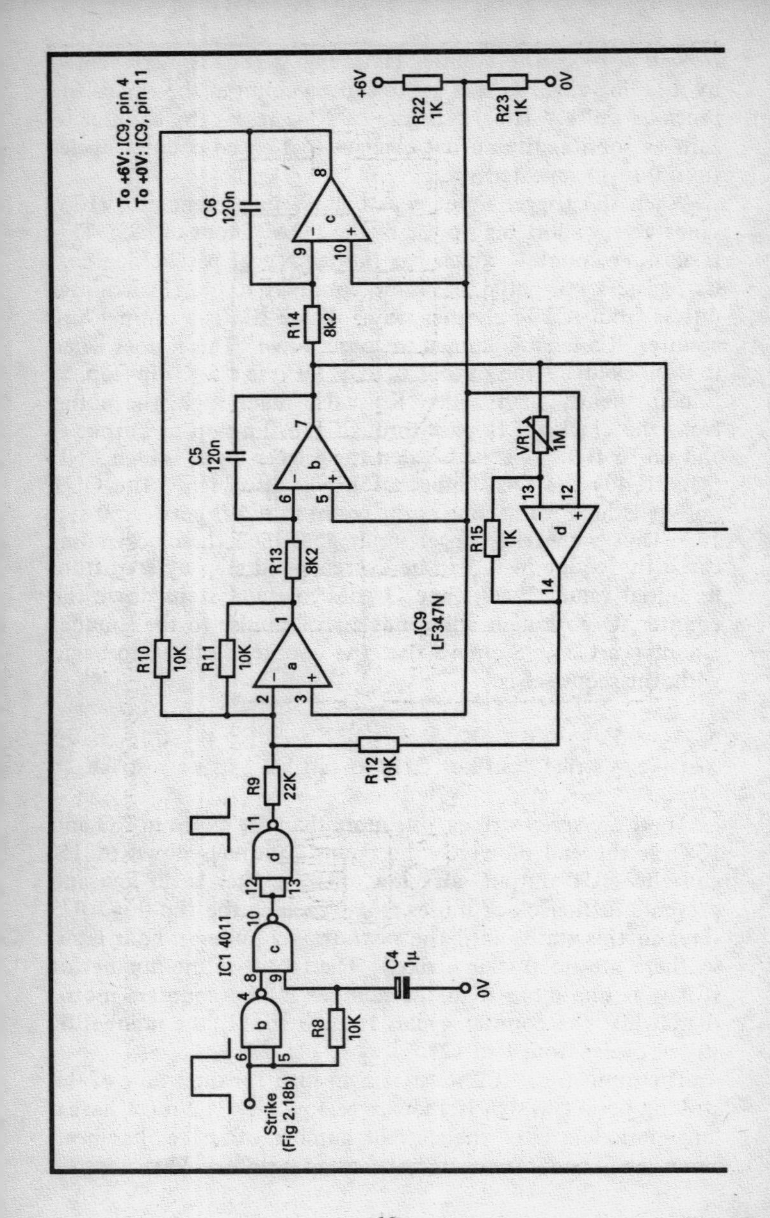
To +6V: IC9, pin 4
To +0V: IC9, pin 11
+6V
0V
R22
1K
R23
1K
C6
120n
R14
8K2
C5
120n
VR1
1M
R15
1K
R13
8K2
IC9
LF347N
R10
10K
R11
10K
R12
10K
R9
22K
IC1 4011
C4
1µ
R8
10K
0V
Strike
(Fig 2.18b)

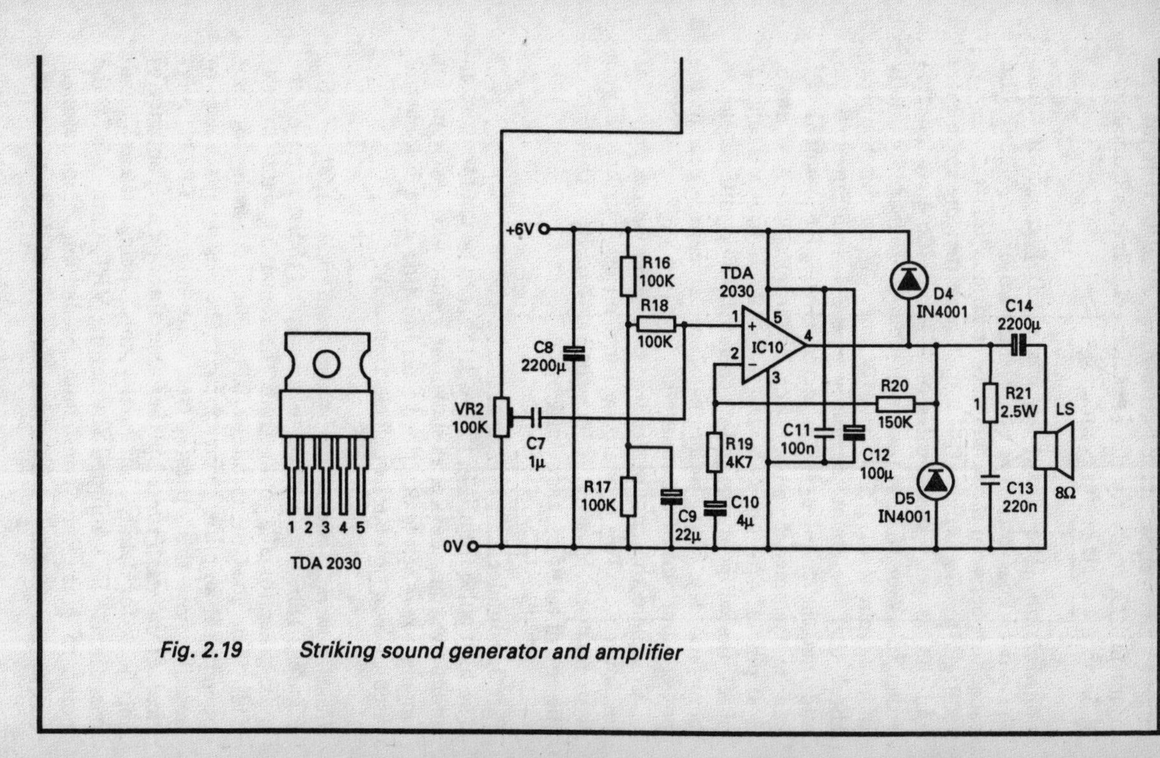

Fig. 2.19 Striking sound generator and amplifier

trigger pulse ends, its negative-going edge increments the count in IC3, ready for the next hour, when it is loaded into IC5 and the cycle begins again.

Construction: The circuit requires a 220μF capacitor where the power lines enter the board, and two or three 22nF disc capacitors between the power lines at various points.

Begin by assembling IC3–IC6. Check that the spare gates and the, as yet, unused gates of IC4 and IC6 are connected either to 0V or +6V. A triggering input is produced by briefly shorting pin 2 of IC2 to the 0V line. When this happens, check that the count previously in IC3 is transferred to IC5 and that the count in IC3 is incremented. The count in IC5 can be examined by monitoring its output pins: A at pin 6, B at pin 11, C at pin 14 and D at pin 2. If IC5 fails to load, check the wiring of the pulse generator. If counting seems to be erratic, try wiring additional 22nF capacitors near to the power input pins of the counters.

Complete the circuit. IC7 is an astable with a period of just over 5s. This is the pace for a majestic strike. If you wish to make it faster, reduce the value of R6. This part of the circuit takes less than 3mA.

Part 3: Sounder

The high pulse from IC8, Figure 2.18b, can be used to drive an audible warning device, as shown in Figure 4.6. A circuit for ringing a *real* bell is described later but first we will look at a circuit which simulates a bell electronically.

How it works: Each strike pulse from the output of IC8, Figure 2.18b, is converted to a shorter (15ms) pulse by the pulse-generator IC1 built from the remaining gates of IC1. This then goes to a state-variable filter, consisting of four operational amplifiers (Fig. 2.19). There is no space here to describe how this operates (see book number BP299, *Practical Electronic Filters* by the same author and publisher as this book for details), but briefly, this is being used as a band-pass filter. It is adjusted (by setting VR1) until it is on the point to going into continuous oscillation at its resonant frequency. A short high pulse to pin 2 of IC9a makes the filter oscillate, but the oscillations begin to die away as soon as the pulse ends. The sound is very much like that of a bell being struck. The frequency of the filter is determined by the values of R13/14 (which must be equal) and C5/6 (which must also be equal). The equation is:

$$f = 0.16/RC$$

In Figure 2.19 the frequency is 162Hz, giving a deeply pitched note suitable for a striking clock. If you prefer a lower or higher pitch, alter the resistors or capacitors accordingly. The amplifier section is a standard audio amplifier, based on the TDA2030.

Construction: The wiring up of IC1 is now to be completed; remove the temporary connections to 0V and+V and re-wire this IC as shown in Figure 2.19. IC9 is a quadruple op amp IC; group the capacitors and ICs closely around it. In general, all leads in this part of the clock, except the speaker leads, should be kept as short as possible. The output side of the amplifier should be kept away from the filter and input side. Note that R21 in the amplifier is rated at 2.5W. IC10 will require a small bolt-on heat-sink, rated at about 20°C/W.

When testing, trigger the circuit by using the output from the strike logic or, more conveniently, a continuous series of pulses at intervals of about 5s. This can be obtained by breadboarding a 7555 IC as in Figure 2.18b, but with R6 = 100kΩ, R7 = 1kΩ and C3 = 22μF. VR1 controls the amount of damping of the filter. Damping is greatest when VR1 is small, the sound then being a dull thud. Increase VR1 until a suitably resounding bell-like sound is produced, but not so much that the filter oscillates permanently. VR2 controls the volume of the sound. Since this resistor loads the filter circuit to a certain extent, you will have to re-adjust VR1 each time VR2 is altered. As the volume of sound is reduced, the note becomes more muffled and loses the initial sharp clanging sound.

To strike a real bell (or to produce novel effects such as a cuckoo emerging from a trap-door) some kind of mechanism involving a solenoid is required. The typical solenoid has a soft-iron core which is pulled into the coil when the current flows. There is a spring to return the core to its original position afterward. The solenoid is arranged so that the core strikes a gong or tubular chime when the coil is energised. Rotary solenoids are also available; if the shaft has a hammer mounted on it, activating the solenoid swings the hammer to strike a gong or bell.

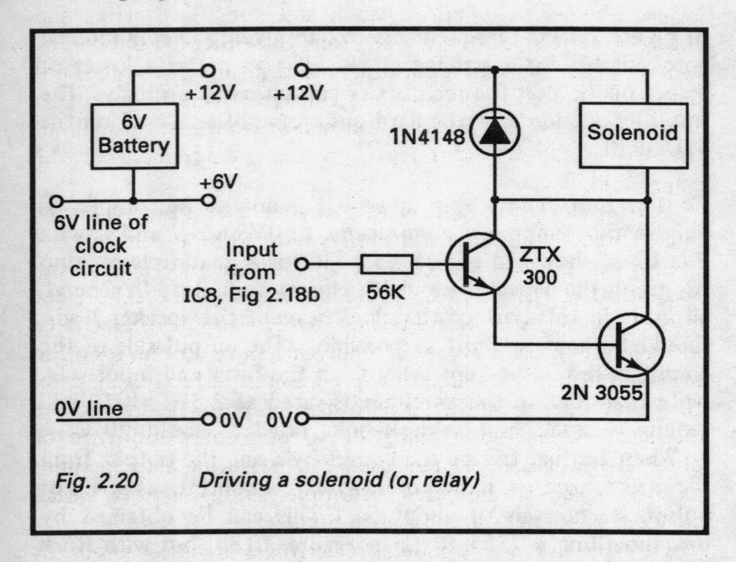

Fig. 2.20 Driving a solenoid (or relay)

Figure 2.20 shows a solenoid driver suitable for use with a small solenoid with a coil resistance of 10Ω or more. Solenoids usually require at least 12V, so an additional 6V battery is required. However, those that nominally require 12V may well provide enough force when run on 6V, particularly if the core is not allowed too far out of the coil. It is worth trying this in order to simplify power requirements. This circuit can also drive a relay, allowing motors, lamps and other electrically powered devices to be switched on each hour.

Another avenue to explore is the use of a relay connected in place of the solenoid (see also, Project 18).

Chapter 3

MEASURING ELAPSED TIME

To measure the time taken for a fairly lengthy event, such as the time for a 10km cross-country race, the easiest method is to use a real-time clock or watch and note the starting and finishing times. Subtract one from the other to obtain the elapsed time. In this application the real-time clock does not have to be set accurately against Universal Time or any other time standard. The fact that it is half-an-hour fast throughout the race makes no difference to the measurement of the elapsed time.

A real-time clock used in this way will give a precise result, but elapsed timing does not always have to be precise. When boiling an egg, we are content to measure the time to the nearest 10 or 20 seconds. There is no need for a precisely-cut crystal and a chain of frequency dividers to give the time to the nearest 0.01s. There are many instances in everyday life in which elapsed timing of low precision is perfectly adequate. How long does it take to walk to the bus stop? to drive to the market? to develop a film? or to perform a sequence of physical exercises? Timers used for measuring elapsed times of these kinds can be based on simpler timing circuits, which are cheaper to make and easier to build.

One of the most popular electronic processes used for timing is the charging of a capacitor. Figure 3.1 shows the basic circuit. Given a constant voltage source V, the capacitor charges at a rate depending on the difference between V and the p.d. V_t across the capacitor. The rate also depends on the resistance (the higher the resistance, the slower the charging) and on the capacitance (the higher the capacitance the slower the charging).

As the capacitor becomes charged, V_t increases. The difference between V and V_t decreases and the rate of charging is gradually reduced. This is why, starting with an uncharged capacitor ($V_t = 0$), the graph for V_t against time rises rapidly at first, then more slowly, and finally very slowly (Fig. 3.2). In theory it *never* reaches V but, in practice, it reaches it so

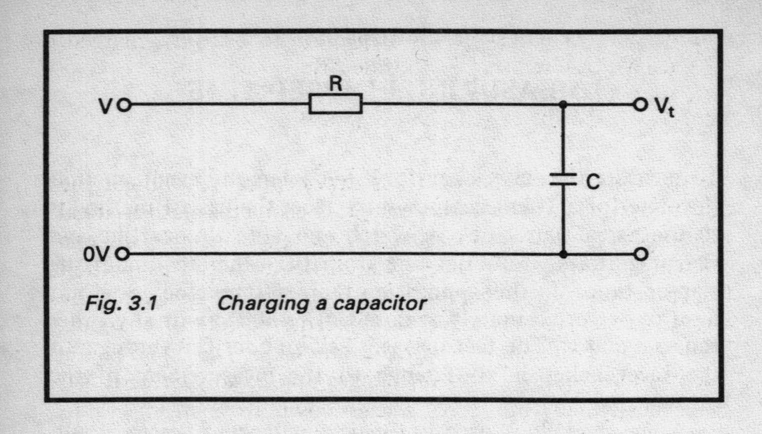

Fig. 3.1 Charging a capacitor

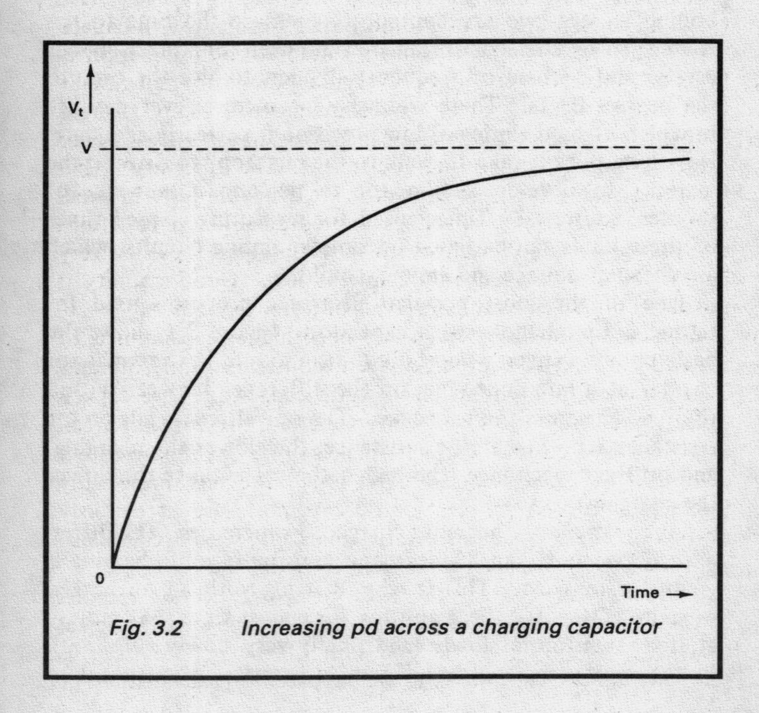

Fig. 3.2 Increasing pd across a charging capacitor

closely that we consider the capacitor to be fully charged.

The equation relating V_t to time t is:

$$V_t = V(1 - e^{-t/RC})$$

We say the rate of rise of V_t is *exponential*. Although the equation is slightly complicated, it is a precise mathematical relationship. If we measure V_t at any instant, we can calculate t, the elapsed time. The difficulty with this method is a practical one. *Precision* is obtainable by designing the circuit so that it is 'tunable' to the required rate of charging. The major problem arises with *stability*. The natural frequency of a quartz crystal changes appreciably after it has been newly cut, but soon settles down to a steady value. Temperature affects frequency severely, but not under the conditions under which most quartz timing circuits are used (page 15). Stability is much more of a problem with capacitors. The most stable capacitors suitable for timing applications are polycarbonate and polystyrene, the latter being made with close tolerance (1%). If temperature is likely to be a problem, NPO ceramic plate capacitors may be used, since these have zero temperature coefficient. The difficulty is that the most stable types of capacitor are available only in small values. Polystyrene capacitors are obtainable up to 10nF, and polycarbonate capacitors up to 470nF (but these are very large). NPO types are only 18pF or less. Good stability is possible only when timing intervals of a few seconds.

For timing longer intervals, we need higher capacitance, of the order of tens, hundreds, or even thousands of microfarads. Tantalum and aluminium electrolytic capacitors have capacitances in this higher range. Unfortunately, they have appreciable leakage current, which makes precise timing more complicated, and makes really long intervals impossibly imprecise. Moreover, electrolytic capacitors are notoriously unstable. Their capacitance varies markedly with age and also with the extent to which the circuit is used.

Obtaining high precision with resistor/capacitor circuits certainly seems more complicated than using a quartz crystal oscillator, where only the precision of the crystal itself is relevant. But, in spite of the apparent disadvantages of capacitors, there are many instances in which they provide a cheap, simple and adequately precise basis for time-keeping. Capacitor charging is used in many of the projects in this chapter but, before looking at these, we will describe ways in which some of the problems with capacitors may be overcome.

Time Keeping with Capacitors

Referring back to the equation for V_t, we can re-write this as:

$$\frac{V_t}{V} = 1 - e^{-t/RC}$$

Suppose that the capacitor is charged for time t and in that time V_t has reached exactly a quarter of V:

$$0.25 = 1 - e^{-t/RC}$$

$$0.25 - 1 = -e^{-t/RC}$$

$$0.75 = e^{-t/RC}$$

Taking natural logarithms of both sides of this equation:

$$\ln 0.75 = -t/RC$$

$$t = -\ln 0.75 \times RC$$

$$t = 0.288RC$$

This equation tells us how long it takes to charge the capacitor to a quarter of V. We can work out similar equations for other fractions of V and, in each case, get a constant multiplied by RC. This quantity RC is known as the *time-constant* of the circuit. For example, if in the circuit of Figure 3.1 we make R = 1kΩ and C = 10μF, the time constant is RC = 1000 × 0.00001 = 0.01. The capacitor charges to a quarter of V in 0.288 × 0.01 = 2.88ms. Note that this time is affected by R and C but not by the value of V.

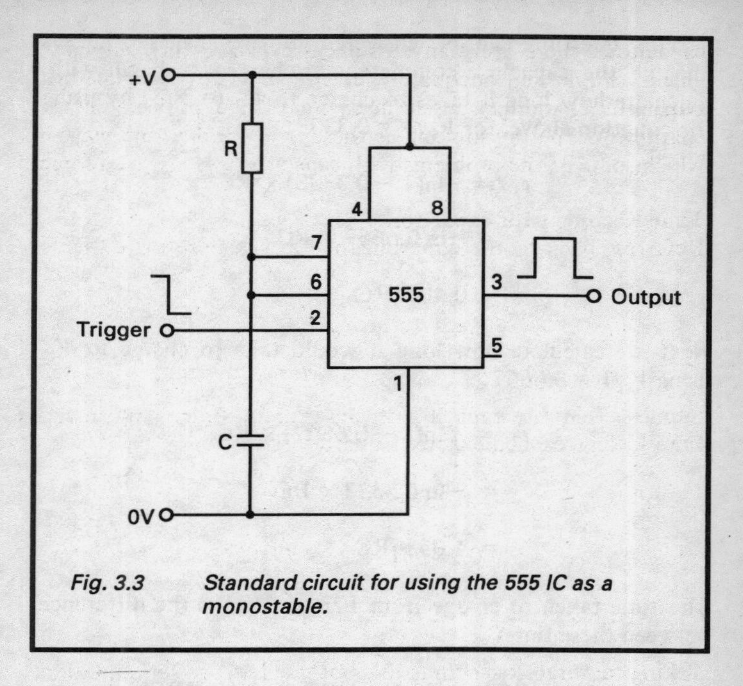

Fig. 3.3 *Standard circuit for using the 555 IC as a monostable.*

There are several circuits that rely on the principle that it takes a fixed and predictable time to charge a capacitor to a given fraction of the supply voltage. The classic circuit uses a resistor and capacitor in conjunction with a 555 timer IC (Fig. 3.3). The supply voltage, equivalent to V in the discussion above may be any value in the range 4.5V to 16V (2V to 18V for the 7555 CMOS version). We begin with the capacitor charged to 1/3 of the supply voltage, so we could say that $V_0 = V/3$. Current flows through R and charges C according to the equation given earlier. The voltage across the capacitor is monitored by an internal circuit connected at pin 6. When the voltage across the capacitor reaches $2V/3$, the capacitor is discharged rapidly, the current flowing away through pin 7. It is discharged until the p.d. across it is reduced to $V/3$ again. We can say that discharge takes place when $V_t = 2V/3$. The question is, how long does it take to charge from V_0 to V_t?

This question can be answered in two stages. Let us imagine the capacitor completely discharged to begin with. Calculate how long it takes to charge to V_0 (= $V/3$) by using the equation above, for $V_0/V = 0.3333$:

$$
\begin{aligned}
t_1 &= -\ln(1 - 0.3333) \times \mathrm{RC} \\
&= -\ln 0.6667 \times \mathrm{RC} \\
&= 0.4054\mathrm{RC}
\end{aligned}
$$

Next we calculate how long it would take to charge to V_t, using $V_t/V = 0.6667$:

$$
\begin{aligned}
t_2 &= -\ln(1 - 0.6667) \times \mathrm{RC} \\
&= -\ln 0.3333 \times \mathrm{RC} \\
&= 1.0986\mathrm{RC}
\end{aligned}
$$

The time taken to charge from $V/3$ to $2V/3$ is the difference between these times:

$$t = (1.0986 - 0.4054)\mathrm{RC} = 0.6932\mathrm{RC}$$

The precision of resistors, capacitors and the level-sensing of the circuit is such that this result is significant in practice to only two significant figures:

$$t = 0.69\mathrm{RC}$$

This is the formula for calculating the time taken. For example, given R = 470Ω and C = 100nF, we find:

$$t = 0.69 \times 470 \times 100 \times 10^{-9} = 32.4\mu\mathrm{s}$$

As before, the value of the supply voltage V does not enter into the equation. This means that the timing is independent of supply voltage. This is important in battery-powered circuits as the voltage varies with the state of the battery. With the 555 timer, a flat battery still produces the correct timing period.

To be able to use this IC in a timing project we have to be able to start its operation, and to know when charging begins and ends. The IC is triggered into action by a low pulse at pin 2. Normally this pin is held at V. To trigger the IC, the voltage must drop below $2V/3$ for an instant. The output from the IC at pin 3 reveals the state of the capacitor. When the capacitor is at $V/3$, the output is low (0V); while the capacitor is charging, the output goes high. Thus the IC when triggered produces a high output pulse lasting 0.69RC seconds.

Pin 4 is connected to the supply in most applications. Its purpose is to reset the timer if required. If the capacitor is charging and output is high, bringing pin 4 below $2V/3$ for an instant reduces the charge on the capacitor to $V/3$ immediately and the output goes low.

Pin 5 is seldom used in timing applications. It connects to the comparator used in detecting voltage levels. By applying a voltage to this pin, we can change the levels at which the capacitor is charged and discharged. This alters the time period.

Longer Periods

As stated above, a large-value capacitor means low precision and possible long-term variations in the timing. This applies equally to the 555 timer. This problem can be overcome by connecting the timer as an astable (Fig. 3.4). This has two resistors so that the capacitor is charged through R_A and R_B but is discharged only through R_B. The charging period (output high) is t_1:

$$t_1 = 0.69(R_A + R_B)$$

The discharging period (output low) is t_2:

$$t_2 = 0.69R_B$$

The total period of charging and discharging is the sum of these and the frequency of the astable is:

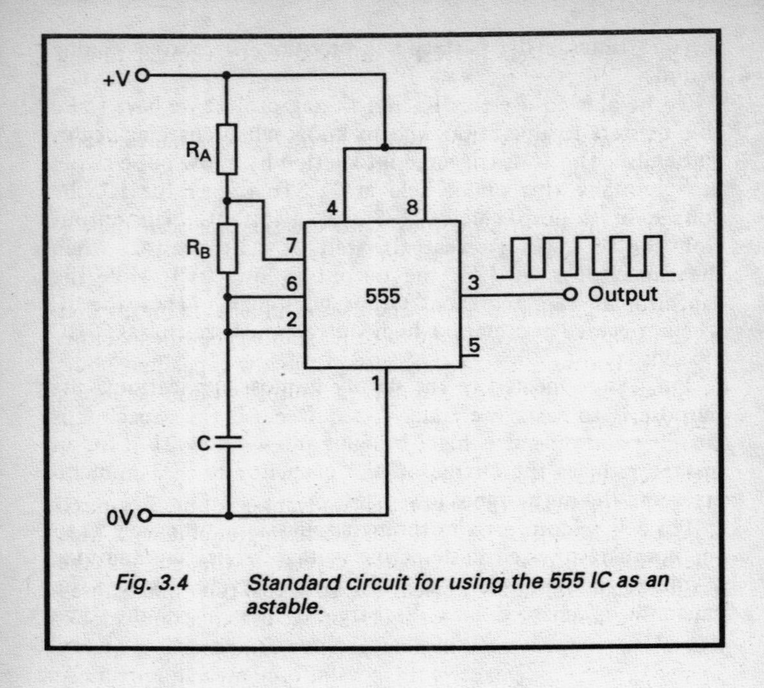

Fig. 3.4 *Standard circuit for using the 555 IC as an astable.*

$$f = \frac{1}{t_1 + t_2} = \frac{1.44}{(R_A + R_B)}$$

By choosing suitable values of R_A, R_B and C, it is possible to produce an astable running at any required frequency (within the range set by the limits imposed on the permissible values of the resistors and capacitor). Having built an astable, the way is clear for timing longer periods. We simply use a frequency-divider chain (page 18) to divide the frequency of the output until we obtain a signal in which the pulses are of the required length. Or, to put it another way, we count a large number of pulses. For example, if the astable runs at 10Hz, we time a period of 30 min by counting 10 × 30 × 60 pulses. A counter is set to zero at the start and the end of the period is indicated when the counter reaches 18 000.

The main reasons for using an astable for elapsed timing are:

* To obtain very long timing periods – perhaps several days long.

* To time shorter periods with greater precision than is possible with a monostable.

In the second case above, the use of an astable means that we can employ a polystyrene or other stable type of capacitor. The astable runs fairly fast because of the low capacitance but, by counting a sufficient number of pulses, we can achieve a relatively long timing period.

High Precision

The 555 and other RC timers have advantages but, for maximum precision, we must use a basic timing circuit with high inherent precision. The quartz crystal is the best of the readily available timing devices for both real-time and elapsed time operations. For highest precision we use an atomic clock. Several of the projects in this chapter are based on quartz crystal timing. Essentially, the crystal oscillates at a precisely known frequency and we count the oscillations or pulses. For elapsed timing, this is not quite as simple as it seems. A counter can count any *whole* number of pulses but not *fractions* of pulses. Suppose the measured interval of time has not ended at the 347th pulse but has ended before the 348th pulse. We can only say that the interval is between 347 and 348 pulses long. If the divided frequency runs at 100Hz, the interval is between 3.47s and 3.48s. But to which length is it nearer? Do we record it as 3.47s, ignoring what might be almost a whole pulse? Or do we record it as 3.48s, when it might be only a little more than 3.47s? If we round the time to 3.5s, this gives the result only to the nearest 0.1s. The timing device is appreciably more precise than this, yet we have lost a degree of precision simply because we have not been able to determine the odd fraction of a pulse. In practice, the situation is more complicated than this for we can not guarantee that a clock pulse will arrive exactly at the beginning of the interval, neither that the interval will end exactly on a clock pulse. There are *two* odd fractions of pulses to be accounted for, one at the beginning and one at the end of the interval.

There are a few ways of solving this problem, all of which rely on high-speed circuitry and so are outside the scope of the projects in this book. It is also unlikely that the typical reader will have any need to employ such highly precise techniques. However, we will describe one of the techniques as an illustration of what can be done to achieve high-precision elapsed timing. The principle is to count the whole number of pulses during the interval and also to estimate the lengths of the short periods that occur at the start and finish.

Figure 3.5 shows how we measure the starting period. The main timing clock (clock 1) delivers pulses at a known rate. These are the pulses that are being counted as whole pulses to determine the approximate length of the interval. The figure shows the interval starting between one pulse and the next. We want to measure the time between the start of the interval and the arrival of the first clock pulse. The technique known as *vernier interpolation*, uses the same principle as the vernier scale on vernier calipers or a micrometer screw gauge. The measuring circuit has another clock, a start-triggered clock (clock 2) which is started *exactly when* the interval begins. The period of clock 2 is slightly longer than that of clock 1. In the diagram, it is 10% longer. The circuit has the means of detecting when a pulse from the main clock coincides with a pulse from the start-triggered clock. In the diagram this occurs on the 4th pulse of each clock. The number of pulses from start to coincidence is counted and we then calculate the start period:

$$\text{Start period} = 4 \times 0.1t$$

where t is the period between one pulse from clock 1 and the next. For greater precision, we can make clock 2 have a period closer to that of clock 1. For example it could be only 1% longer. It takes more counts to reach coincidence and the calculation is:

$$\text{Start period} = n \times 0.01t$$

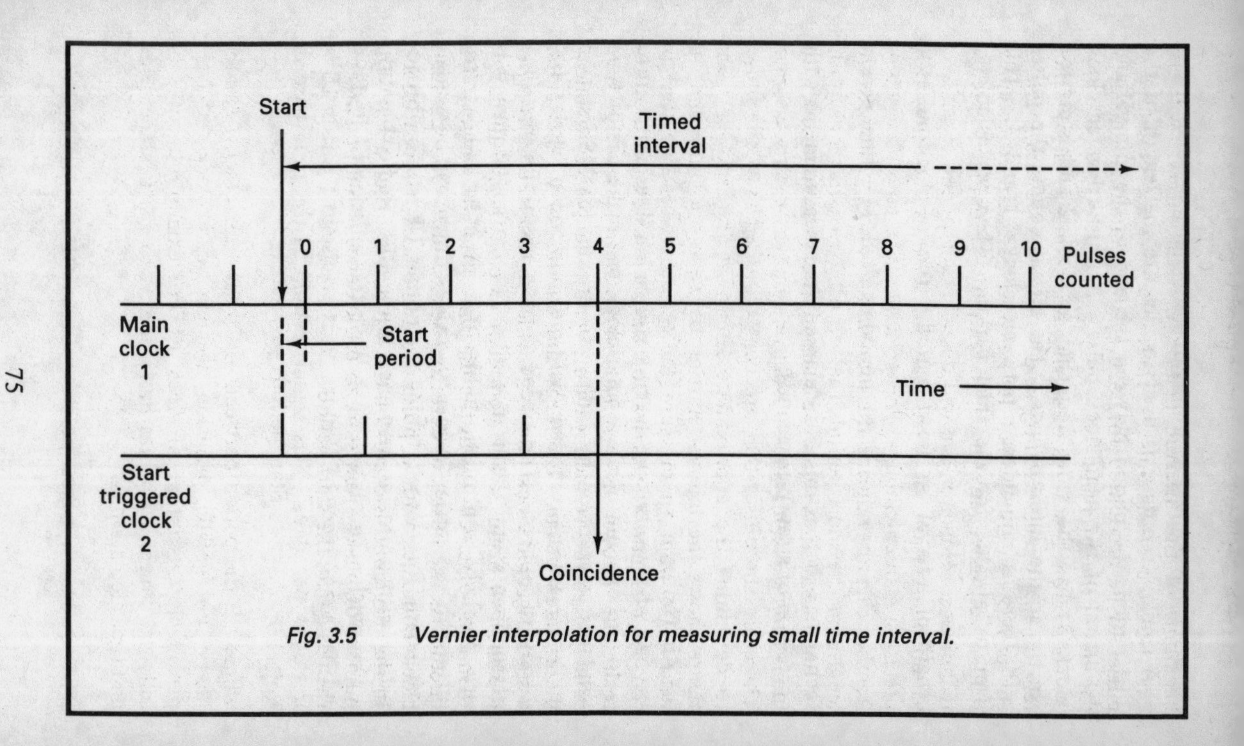

Fig. 3.5 Vernier interpolation for measuring small time interval.

where n is the number of counts to coincidence.

A similar technique is used to measure the length of the final period, the period between the end of the interval and the arrival of the next clock pulse. A finish-triggered clock (clock 3) has the same frequency as clock 2 and is started exactly as the interval ends. The circuit counts the pulses until there is coincidence between clocks 1 and 3. This gives us a value for the final period. Then we calculate:

Length of interval = start period + (no. of clock pulses × period of clock 1) − final period

Techniques such as this allow elapsed time measurements with a precision of a few picoseconds.

Off Air Timing

Anyone who wants a precise time source but does not want to go to the expense of an atomic clock can make use of time standards transmitted by radio. In Britain, the MSF station at Rugby transmits coded real-time data, on a carrier frequency of 60kHz. The coded data is useful for real-time measurements but this is not all. The carrier frequency is very precisely controlled, unlike that of most radio transmitters, so the carrier frequency, divided down, can be used as a standard for elapsed timing. Another UK station broadcasting with a precise frequency is the BBC Radio 4 station at Droitwich. This is the Long Wave transmission of Radio 4 and has a frequency of 198kHz. It is precise to 1 part in 10^{11}, or 864ns per day. This signal is used as the time base in Project 9.

Project 4 – Audible Timer

(Beginner's project)

This is a simply constructed timer circuit which can be set for any period of minutes, from 1 min to 7 min. A rotary switch is used to select the timing period.

The position to which the switch is set is indicated by numerals marked on the panel. The setting can also be determined by counting the 'clicks', beginning with the switch turned fully to the left. There is a push-button which resets the circuit and timing begins from the instant the button is released. At the end of the period there is a loud audible signal from the speaker. This is an intermittent note for maximum impact against a noisy background. The note continues for 1 minute. As well as the sound signal there is a high-intensity LED which comes on during the timing period and flashes when the period ends.

One of the advantages of this timer is that it can be set and run in the dark. This makes it suitable for dark-room timing. It is also ideal as a timer for use by blind persons.

How it works: This timer relies on the principle of obtaining a relatively long timing period by dividing down the frequency of a high-frequency astable, as explained on page 13. The astable is the well-known 555 timer in its CMOS form (IC1, Fig. 3.6). As explained on page 70, the frequency is independent of variations in the level of the supply voltage, so the circuit is ideal for battery operation. The preset resistor VR1 allows the frequency to be set to 273Hz. This provides the alarm tone. The 273Hz signal is divided by the 14-stage counter IC2. At stage 8 of the counter we obtain a signal at approximately 1Hz which is used to make the note intermittent. The timing frequency comes from stage 14 of the IC, at which the astable frequency is divided by 2^{14}, or 16384, giving a frequency of 1/60Hz, or 1 count per minute.

The output from stage 14 is inverted by transistor TR1 and fed to the clock input of a second counter IC3. This is a decade counter with decoded outputs. The outputs of this counter are normally at logical high, except that just one of

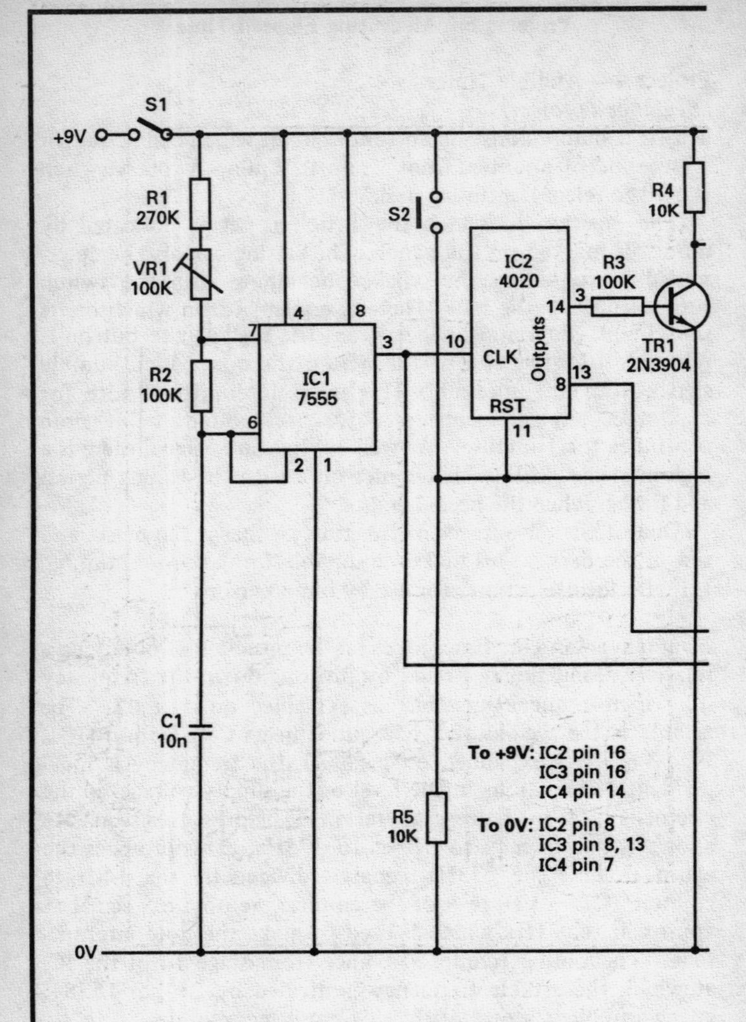

Fig. 3.6 Audible timer.

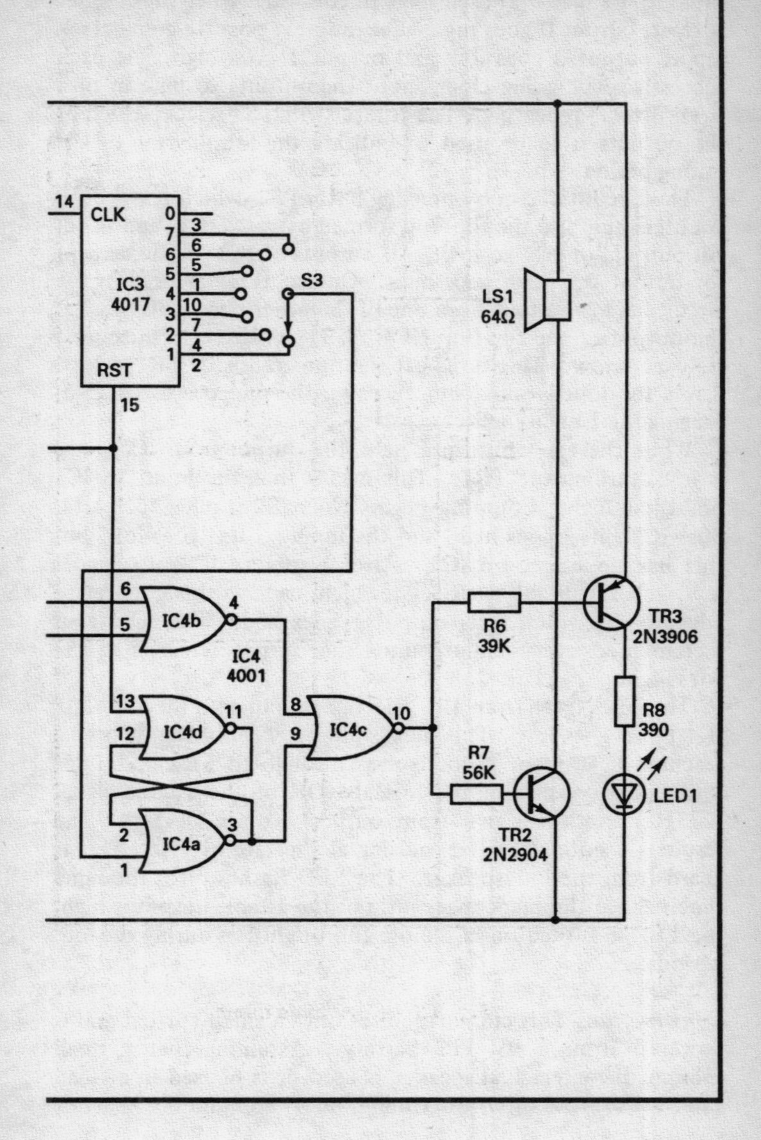
14
CLK
0
7
6
5
4
3
2
1
IC3
4017
RST
15
3
6
5
1
10
7
4
2
S3
LS1
64Ω
6
5
IC4b
4
IC4
4001
13
12
IC4d
11
8
9
IC4c
10
2
1
IC4a
3
R6
39K
R7
56K
TR2
2N2904
TR3
2N3906
R8
390
LED1

the outputs is low at each stage of counting. When the counter is reset, output 0 goes high. On the next positive-going clock input, output 0 goes low and output 1 goes high. At each successive high-going clock input the outputs go high in turn from 0 to 7, repeating. The rotary switch S3 selects which of the outputs is to be used to indicate the termination of the timing period.

The circuit is reset by pressing button S2, which resets both counters and also the flip-flop formed by gates IC4a and IC4d. All outputs of IC2 go low. All outputs of IC3 go low, except for output 0, which goes high. Output 0 is not used in the circuit. A low output from one of the other pins of IC3 makes the output of the flip-flop (IC4 pin 3) go high. The output of IC4c goes low. This turns off the npn transistor TR2, which drives the loudspeaker, but turns on the pnp transistor TR3, causing the LED to light.

While the reset button is held, the output from IC2 pin 3 is low, turning off TR1. This means that the input to IC3 pin 14 is high. Counting begins when S2 is released. After 30s, IC2 pin 3 goes high, and the input to IC3 goes low, but this has no effect on IC3. After 1 minute IC2 pin 3 goes low, and the input to IC3 goes high, causing this counter to advance one count. Its output 1 goes high. The counter is incremented every minute until the output selected by S3 goes high.

The high level from the selected output sets the flip-flop. IC4 pin 3 goes low. This makes pin 9 low, allowing the signal reaching IC4c from IC4b to pass through to TR2 and TR3. This signal consists of the logical NOR of the astable signal (273Hz) and the signal from output 8 of IC2 (1Hz). The result is a note at 273Hz, pulsing at the rate of 1Hz. This is heard from the loudspeaker. The LED flashes on at the same time. Since the mark-space ratio of the astable output is high, the LED is turned on at almost full brightness during the 'on' periods.

Construction: This circuit requires only a small current and is powered from a 9V PP3 battery. Assuming that a small (38mm diameter) loudspeaker is used, it is housed in a small case. For stability of timing, and minimum effect of temperature, use metal-film resistors for R1 and R2 and a polystyrene capacitor for C1.

Assemble the astable circuit and the first counter (IC1 and IC2). Check that all outputs of IC2 go low when S2 is pressed. When S2 is released, a voltmeter shows that the output at pin 13 is approximately 1Hz and that pin 3 changes from high to low or low to high every 30s. Adjust VR1 to obtain this timing. While the remainder of the circuit is being built, it is convenient to use the output from IC2 pin 1 to drive TR1. This runs at 1/15Hz so saving prolonged periods of waiting while testing the circuit.

Wire up TR1 and IC3, and test their operation, then complete and test the remainder of the circuit.

Project 5 – Long Interval Alarm Timer

(Average project)

This timer is capable of timing intervals of hours or even days. The maximum interval is a fortnight. It sounds an alarm when the interval has elapsed. In addition, it sounds a different alarm if any attempt is made to turn it off before the end of the interval. In this way it can convey two messages: "Interval still in progress" and "Interval finished". While it is timing, it uses very little current (2.5mA) so it is suitable for battery operation over prolonged periods.

The circuit was intended as a pill-box reminder, though it has several other applications. If you are having to take pills regularly, it is all too easy to forget exactly when the next dose is due. Conversely, it is easy to forget that a dose has been taken only recently and to attempt to take a second dose too soon, with undesirable effects. The device can not prevent a person taking out too many pills when the pill-box is opened, neither can it make sure that the person actually swallows the pills removed, but, with intelligent use, it is a helpful prompter.

The circuit is housed in a small box serving as the pill-box. A micro-switch activated by the lid of the box lets the circuit know when the box is opened. The warnings are given by an audible sounder and by a pair of flashing LEDs. Shutting the box (presumably after having taken a pill) starts the long-period

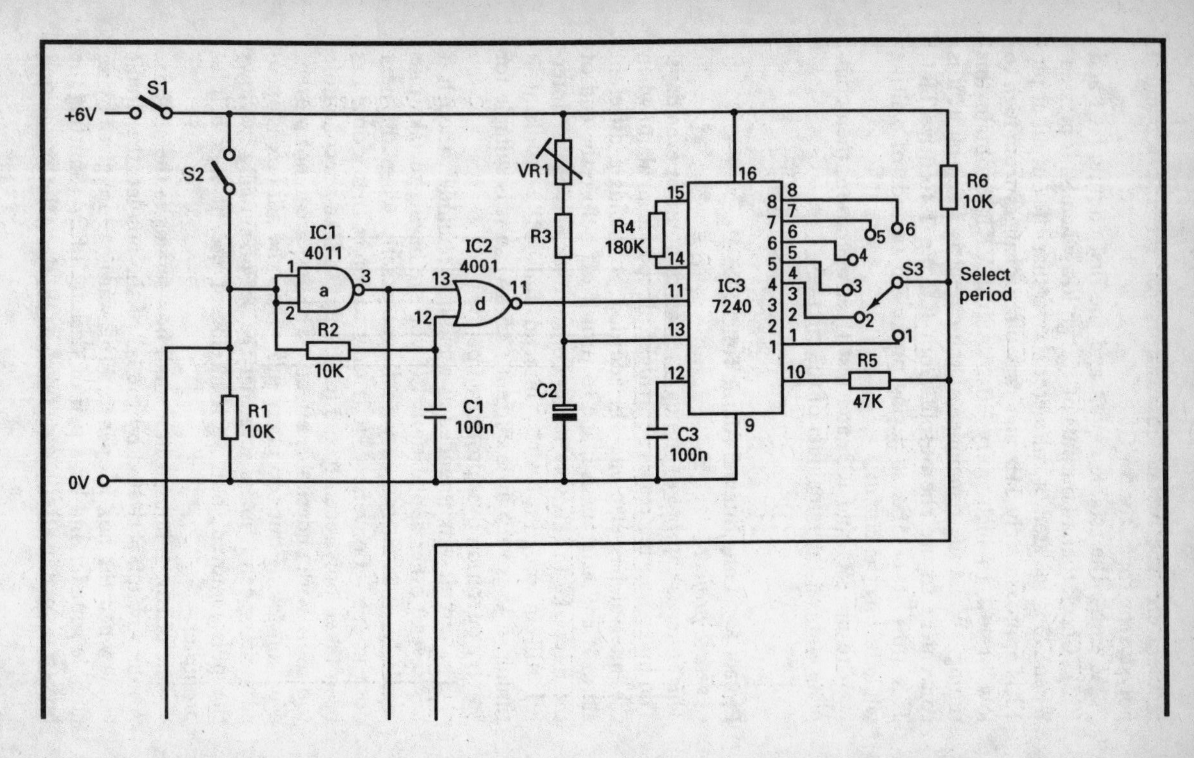
S1
+6V
S2
VR1
R3
R4
180K
R6
10K
IC1
4011
IC2
4001
IC3
7240
S3
Select
period
R2
10K
R5
47K
R1
10K
C1
100n
C2
C3
100n
0V

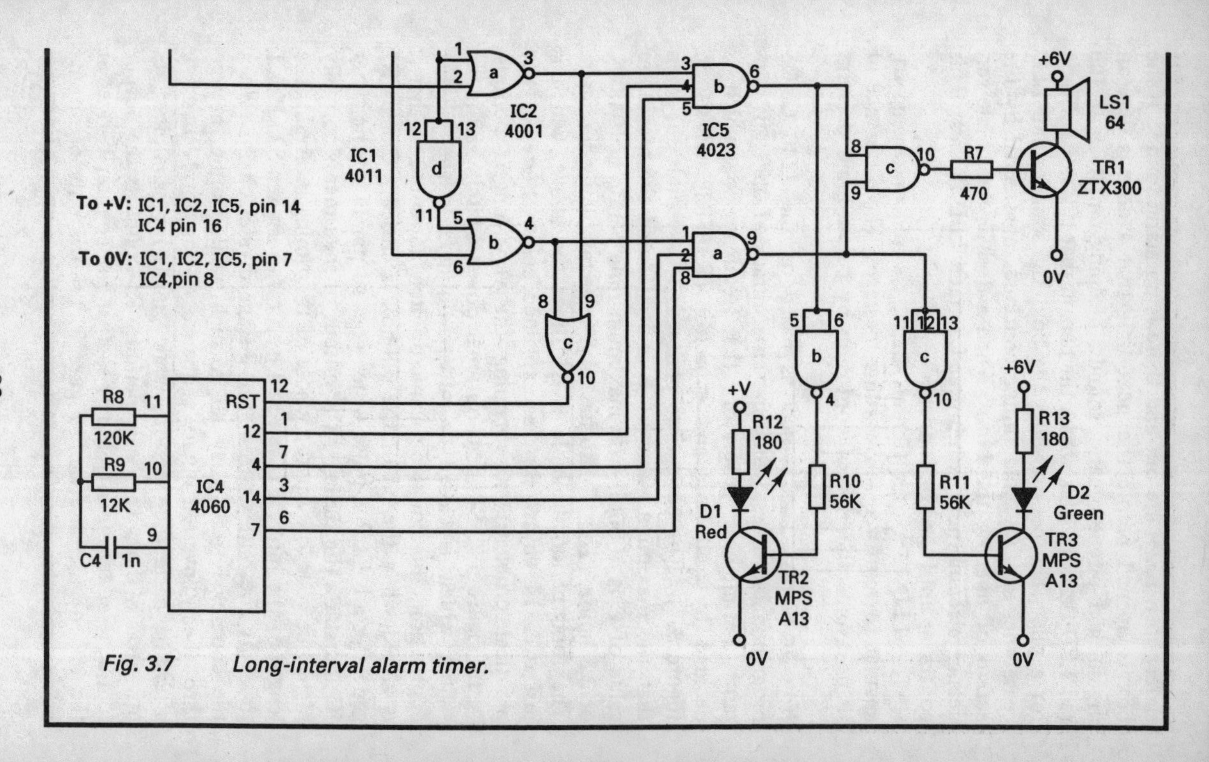

Fig. 3.7 Long-interval alarm timer.

timer; both LEDs are out and there is no alarm sound. If the box is opened before the next time that a dose is due, an urgent high-pitched alarm sounds, bleeping rapidly, and the red LED flashes. This warns the person that it is not yet time for a pill. The person shuts the box, the sounder and LED cease their activity, and timing continues unaffected by the action of opening the box. When a dose is due, a slower, deeper bleeping note is heard and a green LED flashes. This continues until the box is opened.

The LEDs are of different shape, the red one being triangular to reinforce the warning message. The difference of shape avoids the risk of confusion by colour-blind persons.

How it works: This project is based on the 7240 CMOS programmable timer, which has an accuracy of 0.5%. It contains a time-base generator, the frequency of which is decided by a resistor and capacitor (R3/VR1 and C2 in Figure 3.7). The basic time period is RC seconds so, given that the maximum value of R is 10MΩ and the maximum value of C is 1000μF, the maximum time period is 10 000s, or 2.8 hours. The IC also has an 8-stage binary divider chain. The total period available is 2^7 times the above, which is just over 14 days. But, as explained below, there may be practical problems in obtaining the very longest periods.

In Figure 3.7, S1 is an optional power switch. S2 is the switch which is closed to initiate timing. In the pill-box application, this could be a microswitch, mounted so that it is closed when the lid of the pill-box is closed. Closing S2 generates a brief low pulse which goes to pin 11 of the timer IC and starts the timing. The output of the timer is normally high, but goes low for the whole of the timing interval. The length of the interval is selected by a rotary switch S3. Pins 1 to 8 are the outputs from the 8-stage divider chain. When the counter is reset they all go high, while timing they go through an inverted binary sequence. Thus pin 1 goes low after the basic time period, while pin 4, for example, goes low after 8 times the basic period. R5 connects the output to the reset terminal (pin 10) so that the counter is reset at the end of the interval. Figure 3.7 shows only 6 outputs being used; this is sufficient for the pill-box application (see later), but there is no reason why all 8 outputs or any combination of fewer outputs should not be selected. For a single-period timer, omit S3 and wire the chosen output directly to the junction between R5 and R6.

The first stage of the logic consists of two NOR gates and a NAND gate wired as an inverter. These detect the two alarm states. Gate IC2a goes high (at pin 3) when S2 is open (box open) and the IC3 is timing (output low). This is the state of opening the box while the timing interval is in progress. Gate IC2b goes high (at pin 4) when S2 is closed and the output of IC3 is high. This is the state after the end of the interval if the box remains unopened.

A high output on either pin 8 or pin 9 causes a low output from Gate IC2c (pin 10). This makes the reset input of IC4 low. IC4 is a 14-stage counter with its own oscillator, which begins to oscillate when the reset is made low. The oscillator has a period of about 25kHz, which is divided down to produce 1.6kHz at pin 7 (high-pitched note), 200Hz at pin 6 (low-pitched note), 6Hz at pin 1 (fast bleeping), and 1.5Hz at pin 3 (slow bleeping). The remainder of the logic consists of gates producing the fast high-pitched bleep signal, which goes to the red LED D1 by way of TR2, and the slower low-pitched bleep, which goes to the green LED D2 by way of TR3. Both signals go to the speaker LS1 by way of TR1.

Construction: The project is built on a board only 10cm by 6cm. With a miniature loudspeaker (38mm diameter) the unit is housed in a reasonably small box. Since it requires only 2.5mA, it runs for about a month on a set of four AA alkaline cells. There are only 3 logic gate ICs, IC1 (2-input NAND, 4011), IC2 (2-input NOR, 4001) and IC5 (3-input NAND, 4023) and all gates are used. The gates belonging to these 3 ICs are scattered in ones and twos all over the circuit diagram but can easily be identified by their symbols.

Begin with the trigger circuit IC1a/IC2d and timer IC3, and their associated resistors and capacitors. For use as a pill-box timer, with a maximum interval of 8 hours (IC3, pin 8) values for the timing components are R3 = 3.3MΩ, VR1 = 2.2MΩ and C3 = 47μF. Use a tantalum capacitor for C3. The tolerance of these is ±20%, but VR1 allows timing to be adjusted to accommodate this. The main problem with tantalum (and aluminium electrolytic capacitors) is that they have an appreciable leakage current. The effect of this is that charging times tend to be longer than those calculated by multiplying R and C together. As a rule, tantalum capacitors have lower leakage than aluminium electrolytics. The most commonly available types have a leakage of 0.02μA per volt per μF, with a minimum leakage of 1μA. Low-leakage types are available with half this leakage, though such types are not widely stocked. The leakage quoted above is for a capacitor operating at its maximum working voltage; leakage is markedly reduced when operated at a lower voltage. The voltage across the capacitor in this project ranges from 1.6V to 4.2V, but the working voltage is likely to be 16V or even 20V for a 47μF capacitor. This helps to keep leakage to an acceptable level. Using a 47μF tantalum capacitor with resistances totalling 5MΩ or more is feasible. If really long intervals are required, make the resistor less than the calculated value.

Having settled on a suitable value for R3, adjust VR1 until an interval of 225s is obtained with S3 switched to the calibration position, position 1. This gives intervals of 8h, 4h, 2h, 1h and 30min from pins 8 to 4. Other values of R3 and C3 may be substituted for other applications.

Next assemble the oscillator circuit, IC4 with resistors and capacitor. A voltmeter monitoring the output at pin 14 confirms that this works correctly when pin 12 is made low. Assemble the rest of the logic and check that the outputs at IC1 pins 4 and 10 and IC5 pin 10 behave as described earlier. Finally, add the transistor switches. TR2 and TR3 are shown in the figure as single npn transistors, but the MPSA13 is a high-gain Darlington transistor. High-intensity LEDs are preferred but a red triangular one of normal intensity may be used for D1.

Project 6 – Easy Analogue Timer
(Beginner's project)

The project is described as easy because it is easy to construct and because the analogue display is easy to read. The timer is ideal as a telephone timer or for any other application when

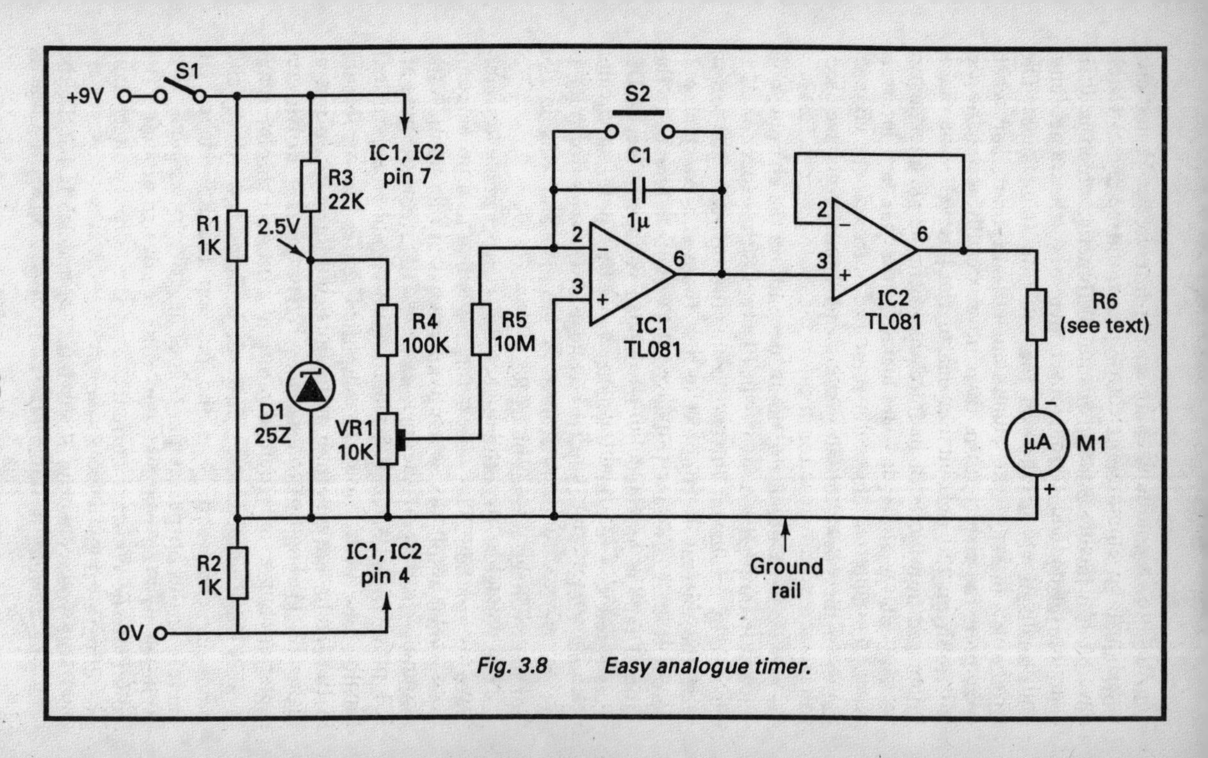

Fig. 3.8 Easy analogue timer.

you want to know how much of the interval has passed and how much is still to come. Using an ordinary digital watch for this can involve a lot of mental arithmetic, which is difficult, especially when trying to converse at the same time. This analogue timer tells you the situation at a glance. The display is a meter, with a needle which begins on the left when you press the reset button, then moves steadily across the dial to finish on the right at the end of the interval. The dial is graduated in minutes or in fractions of the whole interval, or, as a telephone timer, it is graduated in the standard intervals by which calls are charged. Press the button as the connection is made; the needle shows how many units you have used.

How it works: Once again, timing depends on the charging of a capacitor through a resistor. In Figure 3.8 the capacitor C1 is charged by a *constant* current flowing through R5. The reason that the current is constant is that there is a constant p.d. across R5. A constant voltage of 2.5V (with reference to the ground rail) is provided by a band-gap voltage reference D1. This is reduced to a much smaller value by a potential divider R4 and VR1. Typically, the voltage at the wiper of VR1 is set to 0.025V with reference to ground, and this is the constant voltage at one end of R5.

The voltage at the other end of R5 is zero, again with reference to ground. The reason for this is due to a property of operational amplifiers, when connected as in this circuit. The non-inverting input of the amplifier (IC1) connected with feedback from the output behaves as a *virtual ground.* What really happens is that the amplifier senses the difference between the potentials at its inputs and adjusts its output so as to make this difference zero. The current arriving at pin 2 from R5 can not flow *into* pin 2 because this input has a very high impedance. Instead, it flows toward C1 and gradually charges it. As the p.d. on the R5 side of C1 increases, the output at pin 6 goes negative by as much as is required to keep pin 2 at zero volts relative to ground. The result of the constant current is that the output voltage falls steadily; this is known as a *ramp.*

If the voltage across R5 is 0.025V, and R5 is 10MΩ, the charging current is $0.025/(10 \times 10^6) = 2.5$nA. Charge is accumulating at the rate of 2.5nC (nanocoulomb) per second. Given that the capacitance is 1μF, the rise of p.d. across C1 in 1 second is V = Q/C = 2.5mV per second. Because the potential at pin 2 is held at zero, the output voltage falls by this amount. A fall of 2.5mV/s means, for example, that in 10 minutes the voltage falls to –1.5V. This is a conveniently measurable amount, and indicates the sort of timing period for which this circuit is suitable. Since the reference voltage is produced by a voltage reference device, timing is not affected by the state of the battery.

The output of IC1 goes to IC2, which is wired as a voltage follower. As the voltage at pin 3 falls, the output of IC2 falls by exactly the same amount, so as to keep pins 2 and 3 at the same voltage, but its output has low impedance. To connect the meter directly to IC1 draws excessive current from the feedback loop, resulting in an increase of output voltage. IC2 takes virtually no current from the feedback loop and provides ample current to drive the meter without error.

The function of S2 is to reset the timer. It short-circuits and discharges the capacitor. The output of IC1 immediately goes to zero so as to bring pins 2 and 3 to equal voltages.

Construction: The project is intended to be battery powered (it requires only 2mA) and to be housed in a small case so that it takes up little room by the telephone. A 9V battery of the PP3 type is small, yet provides enough voltage to drive the two op amps. The values given for R5 and C1 are suitable for most practicable timing periods.

Assuming that these values will give the interval required, assemble the whole circuit, with the exception of R6 and M1. With the ICs specified, the output of the circuit can fall to –2.25V without being driven too near to the supply rail and affecting accuracy. The equation for the ramp generator is:

$$V_{OUT} = -\frac{V_{REF}t}{RC}$$

where V_{REF} is the divided-down reference voltage at the wiper of VR1. If R and C have the values of Figure 3.8, this equation is simplified to:

$$V_{OUT} = -\frac{V_{REF}t}{10}$$

or
$$V_{REF} = -\frac{10V_{OUT}}{t}$$

If you decide to make a 10-minute (600s) timer, with full scale deflection –2.25V, the equation gives:

$$V_{REF} = -\frac{10 \times -2.25}{600} = \frac{22.5}{600} = 0.0375\text{V}$$

Adjust VR1, with a voltmeter connected between the ground line and the junction of R4/VR1, until you obtain a reading of 0.0375V. This adjustment assumes that R5 and C1 are close to their nominal values, and it will be necessary to re-adjust VR1 later during the final calibration.

The next step is to calculate the value of R6. To keep the timer small in size, and also to save cost, it is suggested that the meter should be a compact moving-coil panel meter. In the catalogues, such meters are listed as 'compact meters', 'signal strength meters' or 'status indicators'. These are all inexpensive microammeters with a full-scale deflection I_{FS} of a few hundred microamps and a coil resistance R_C of a few hundred ohms. Note these values from the catalogue for use when calculating R6:

$$\text{R6} = \frac{V_{OUT} - I_{FS}R_C}{I_{FS}}$$

For example, if $I_{FS} = 200\mu\text{A}$, $R_C = 400\Omega$, and V_{OUT} is intended to be 2.25V (ignore the minus sign as the meter is connected with *positive* terminal to the ground line), then:

$$R = \frac{2.25 - 200 \times 10^{-6} \times 400}{200 \times 10^{-6}} = 10850\Omega$$

R6 should be 10kΩ. The fact that this is a little less than the calculated value is compensated for by re-adjusting VR1 to reduce the voltage at its wiper.

With R6 and M1 connected into the circuit, run the timer several times comparing its display reading with a clock or watch. Adjust VR1 until the needle reaches the maximum scale value at the correct time.

Project 7 – Yoga/Exercise Timer
(Average project)
When you are performing Yoga or physical exercises of various kinds you often need to hold a given position or to repeat a movement for a definite length of time. In practice, it is difficult to estimate intervals of 10 seconds or more with a sufficient degree of precision. Trying to count seconds mentally or keeping one eye on a clock is counterproductive in an activity that is supposed to be relaxing. This device emits a brief restful tone every 10 seconds, allowing you to time intervals of 10s or multiples of 10s with the minimum of distraction.

How it works: Timing is provided by IC1 (Fig. 3.9) which is a 7555 timer IC connected in astable mode (page 71). Its output is normally high, interrupted by a brief low pulse every 10s. VR1 is used to adjust the interval and it is possible to set the device to give intervals shorter than 10s if required. The low pulse goes to the band-pass filter circuit based on IC2. This is the same circuit as was used to produce the chiming sound in Project 3 (see page 52), but here gives a note more like that of a plucked wire. The output signal of the filter passes through VR3, C4 and R12, and is amplified by IC3.

Construction: The size of the enclosure is determined mainly by the diameter of the speaker, LS1. A miniature speaker

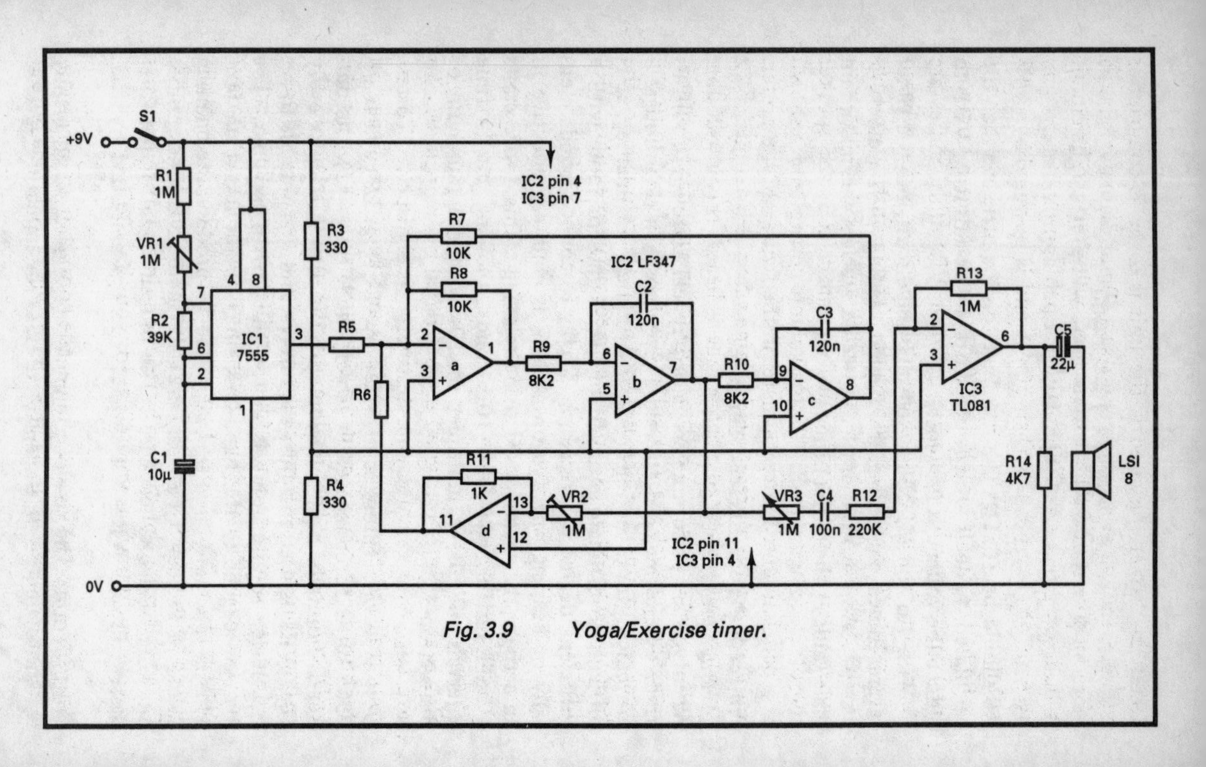

Fig. 3.9 Yoga/Exercise timer.

38mm in diameter is used if the unit is to be as compact as possible, though a larger speaker (say 80mm diameter) gives a more mellow sound which some users will prefer. The circuit is built on a piece of stripboard or a pcb approximately 4cm by 6cm. It requires less than 50mA and is powered by a PP3 battery.

Build the timer circuit first (IC1 and associated components) and check its operation. Adjust VR1 until pulses are obtained at 10s intervals. Then build the filter which is based on a single IC comprising 4 op amps. The resonant frequency of the filter is 162Hz. Reduce R9 and R10 to obtain a higher pitch if preferred. Finally connect IC3, the speaker and other components. VR3 is a volume control and is shown as a panel-mounted potentiometer in the figure. If you prefer, replace this with a preset of the same value. First adjust VR2 so that a fairly damped ringing tone is heard; this is a double tone. Then adjust VR3 to obtain the required volume, remembering that the full volume is not developed until the speaker is mounted. Changing VR3 alters the resonance of the filter to some extent, so it may be necessary to re-adjust VR2 slightly.

Project 8 – Reaction Timer

(Beginner's project)

This is an easily constructed project based on a single IC. To save cost, you can use your testmeter as a display. To test your reaction time, watch the LED and keep one finger on the button. Press and hold the button as soon as you see the LED come on. The reading on the meter tells you the reaction time. There are many ways you can vary this procedure, measuring reaction time for different people or under different conditions. Does it vary at different times of day? Does it depend on age? Is it affected by having loud music played at the same time? Is it affected if you try to watch TV at the same time? Try the reaction time of different parts of your body, such as your elbow or your big toe!

How it works: The circuit is under the control of an operational amplifier wired as an astable (IC1c, Fig. 3.10). The output

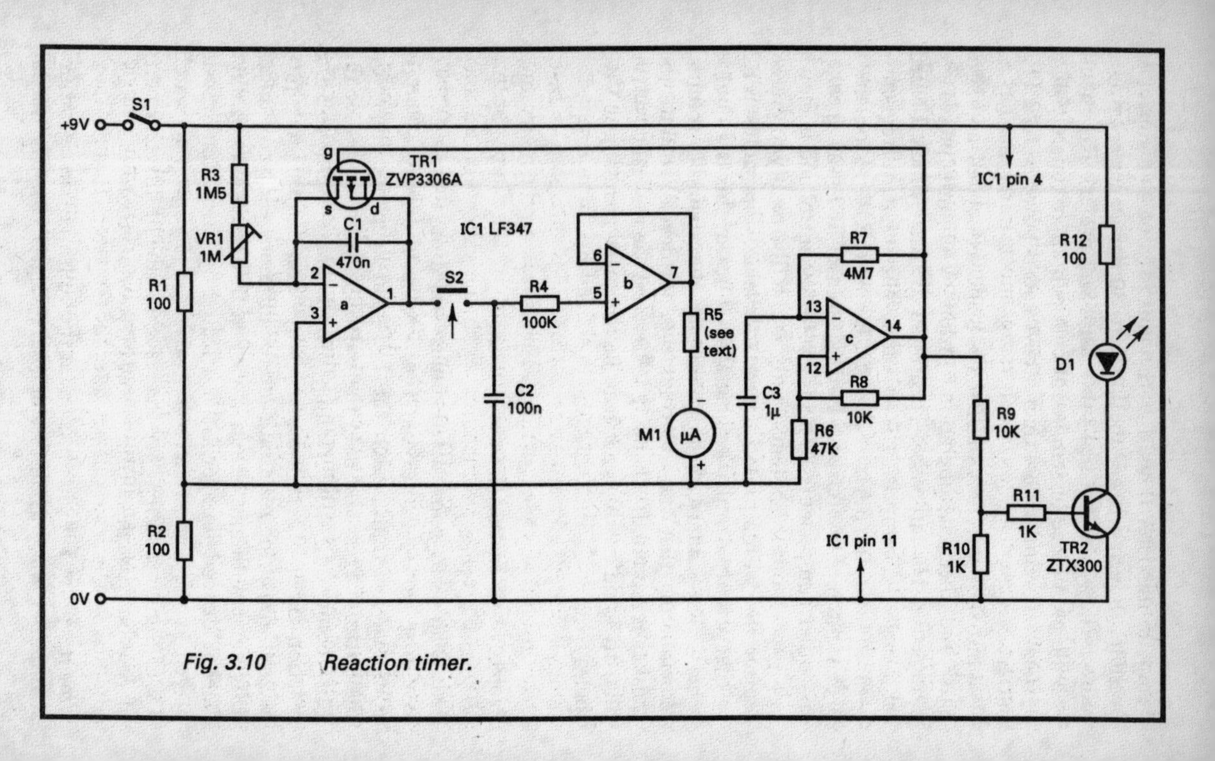

Fig. 3.10 Reaction timer.

of this (pin 14) alternately goes high (9V) for about 5s and then low for about the same time. When it goes high, TR2 is turned on and the LED lights. Timing begins at the same instant. Timing depends on an op amp wired as a ramp generator. The principle is the same as that described on page 88, except that this circuit ramps much faster and has a different technique for resetting the generator. Instead of the switch S2 of Figure 3.8, there is a p-channel enhancement-type MOSFET, TR1. When the output of IC1c goes high (lamp on), the transistor is turned off; the capacitor C1 begins to charge and the output of IC1a ramps down. When the output of IC1c goes low, TR1 is turned on, short circuiting and discharging C1 and so resetting the generator.

S2 is a press-to-open push-button. If this is not pressed, the output voltage of IC1b equals that of IC1a and can be read on the meter. IC1b starts the ramp at 4.5V and ramps down to about 1.5V, but the meter is connected with reverse polarity to the 4.5V rail, so its reading starts at 0V and ramps up to about 3V. When S2 is pressed, IC1b is disconnected from IC1a. The voltage present at that instant is held on C2. In other words, IC1b together with C2 and R4 forms a sample-and-hold circuit. Pressing the button holds the ramp voltage at the instant of your reaction. This is read on the meter and indicates the interval between the start of the ramp and the instant of pressing the button. With the values for R3 and VR1 shown in Figure 3.10 the ramp can be adjusted to 5V per second. The reading never reaches 5V because the IC can not swing that far. An interval of 0.5s is sufficient for most reactions and in this time the ramp reaches 2.5V.

M1 could be a voltmeter reading up to 2.5V or a multimeter switched to a suitable voltage range. In either of these cases the series resistor R5 is not required. If M1 is a microammeter, you will need R5, its value being calculated according to the equation on page 90.

Construction: The specified IC has four op amps of which we use three. You can instead use three ICs, each with a single amplifier. The exact type does not matter, though they should have JFET inputs. This is a compact circuit powered by a small PP3 battery so the project may be housed in a small case, the minimum size being mainly limited by the size of the meter, if one is fitted.

First mount R1 and R2 so that a 4.5V rail is available for the ICs. Then assemble the ramp generator, IC1a and associated components as far as S2. Connect a voltmeter between pin 1 and the 0V line. Also connect a temporary flying lead to the gate of TR1. When the flying lead is touched to the 0V line, the meter goes instantly to 4.5V and stays there. When the flying lead is touched to the +9V line, the output ramps down from 4.5V to about 1.5V. You may prefer to wire a larger capacitor (say 10μF) in parallel with C1 at this stage to make the action easier to follow.

Next assemble the sample-and-hold generator, based on IC1b. Monitor the output of this with a voltmeter, as for IC1a. With S2 not pressed, the output goes to 4.5V or ramps down, depending on the voltage at the gate of TR1. It behaves exactly as the output of IC1a. If S2 is pressed, the voltage remains constant until S2 is released again.

Assemble the astable IC1c. Its output alternates between about 8V and 1.5V. This is dropped down by the potential divider R9/R10 so that T2 and the LED are switched on and off once every 10 seconds. When the connection is made from pin 14 of IC1 to the gate of TR1, the circuit is complete and operates as described above.

If you are using a voltmeter or multimeter, taking the reading from the scale and divide it by 5 to get the time in seconds. For example, a reading of 1.5V is equivalent to a 0.3s reaction time. If you have installed a microammeter, re-calibrate its scale to read seconds directly.

Accuracy: This is intended as an easily-built fun project so great accuracy is not essential. To measure times really accurately, we need a more elaborate circuit, such as that of Project 11 or 13. However, the circuit may be roughly calibrated by connecting, say, four 470nF capacitors in parallel with C1. The ramp is 5 times slower and takes 2.5s to ramp to 2.5V. This period is easier to measure, using a watch or clock for comparison. Then remove the extra capacitors. Better still, if you have a capacitance meter, measure the capacitance of a large-value electrolytic or tantalum capacitor and connect this in parallel with C1. Adjust VR1 until the time to ramp to 2.5V is 0.5 × (0.47 + C) seconds where C is the capacitance in microfarads.

The ramp rate also depends on the input voltage as shown by the equation on page 90. Here the input voltage is 4.5V and falls as the battery ages. Given a fresh battery and if VR1 is adjusted to give the correct ramp rate as near as we can manage it, the circuit is accurate for *comparative* readings. If, for example, the meter shows that person A has a reaction time of 0.8s and B has a time of 0.6s, we can say with certainty the B's time is three-quarters of A's time. Also we can measure by what proportion reaction times are affected by circumstances.

Project 9 – Off Air Frequency Receiver

(Average project)

The BBC Radio 4 Long Wave transmitter at Droitwich operates at a precisely regulated frequency of 198kHz. The timing is accurate to 1 part in 10^{11} (0.86ms per day). In this project we receive the radio signal and use it to drive various timers.

Although this time source is far more precise than is necessary for most purposes, it can be decidedly advantageous for timing in conditions of low or high temperature (page 15). There is also the novelty value of owning a clock which has a remote atomic clock as its ultimate source of timing.

How it works: The signal is received by a ferrite-rod aerial with a coil wound around it (L1, Fig. 3.11) In conjunction with the two parallel capacitors C1 and C2, it is part of a tunable loop. The circuit is tuned by adjusting the variable trimmer capacitor C2. The loop oscillates at radio-frequency (198kHz) which is amplitude modulated by the audio-frequency programme signal. The audio-frequency signal is detected and amplified by the ZN416 radio receiver IC. This is not an essential part of the timer but, by listening to its output with an earphone (TL1), we known that we are tuned to the correct transmission.

For use in the timer, the r.f. oscillations of the loop are detected by a differential amplifier consisting of two radio-

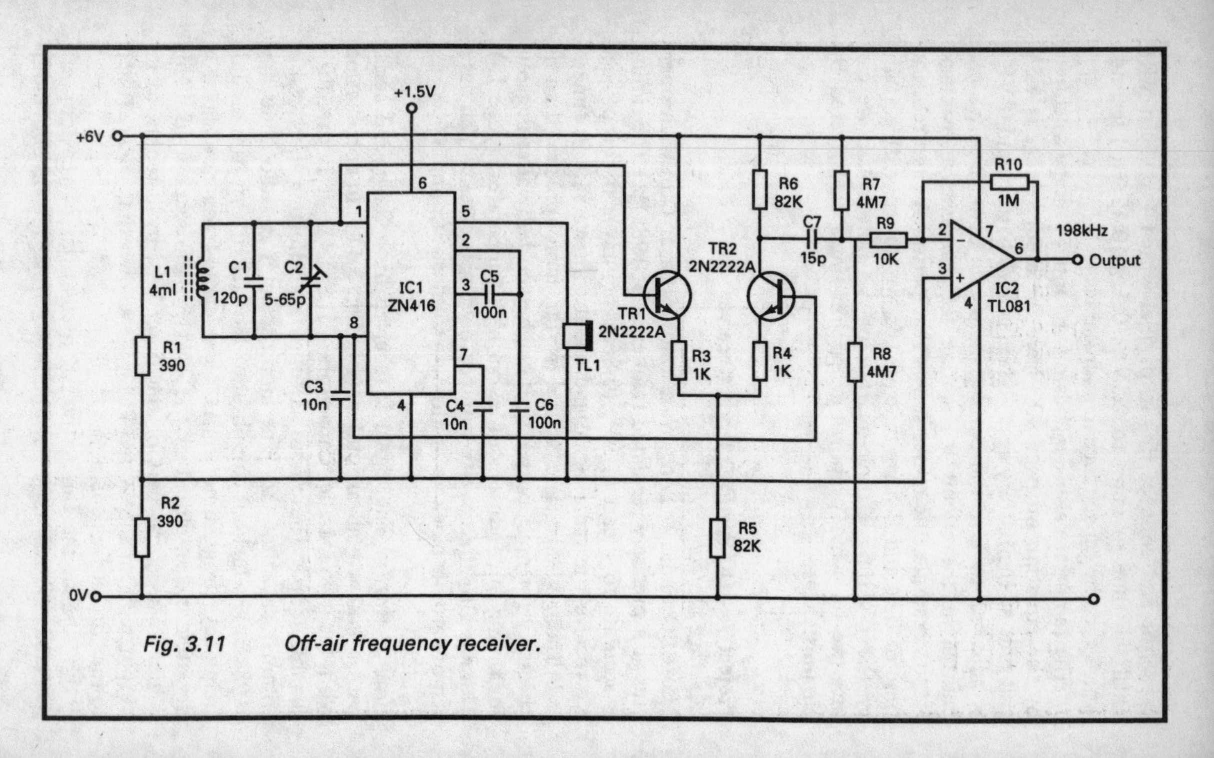

Fig. 3.11 Off-air frequency receiver.

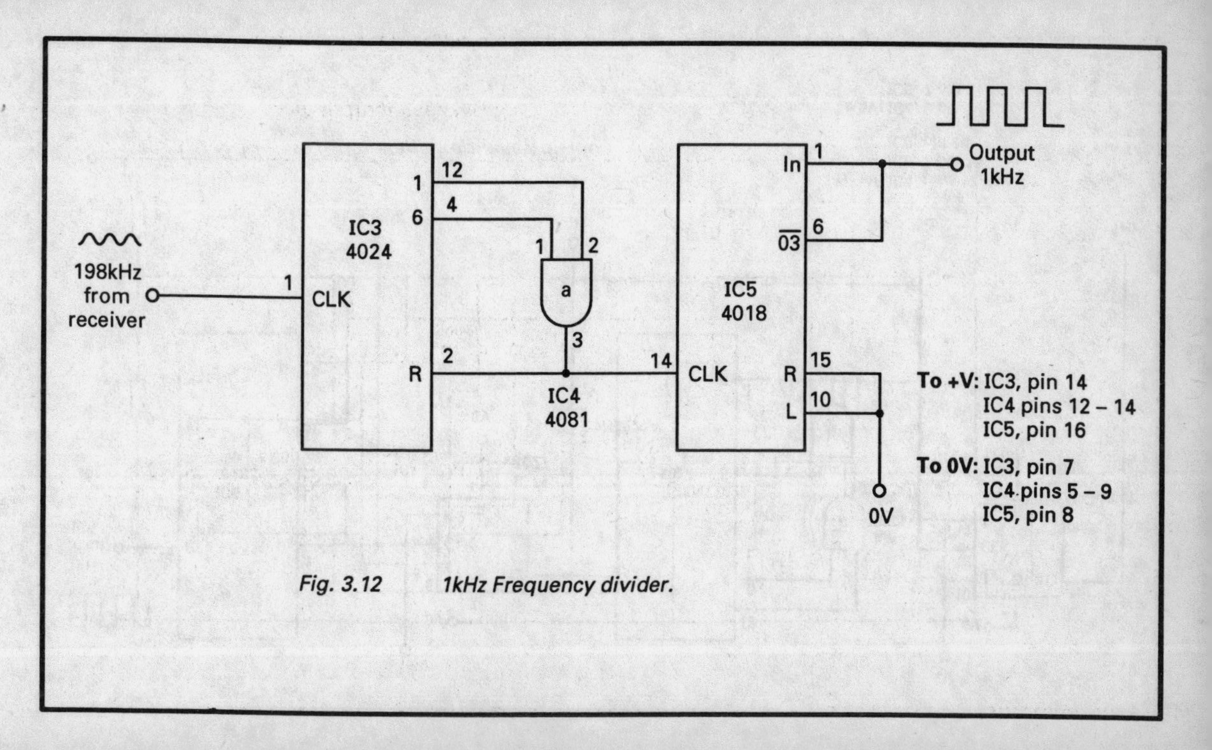

Fig. 3.12 1kHz Frequency divider.

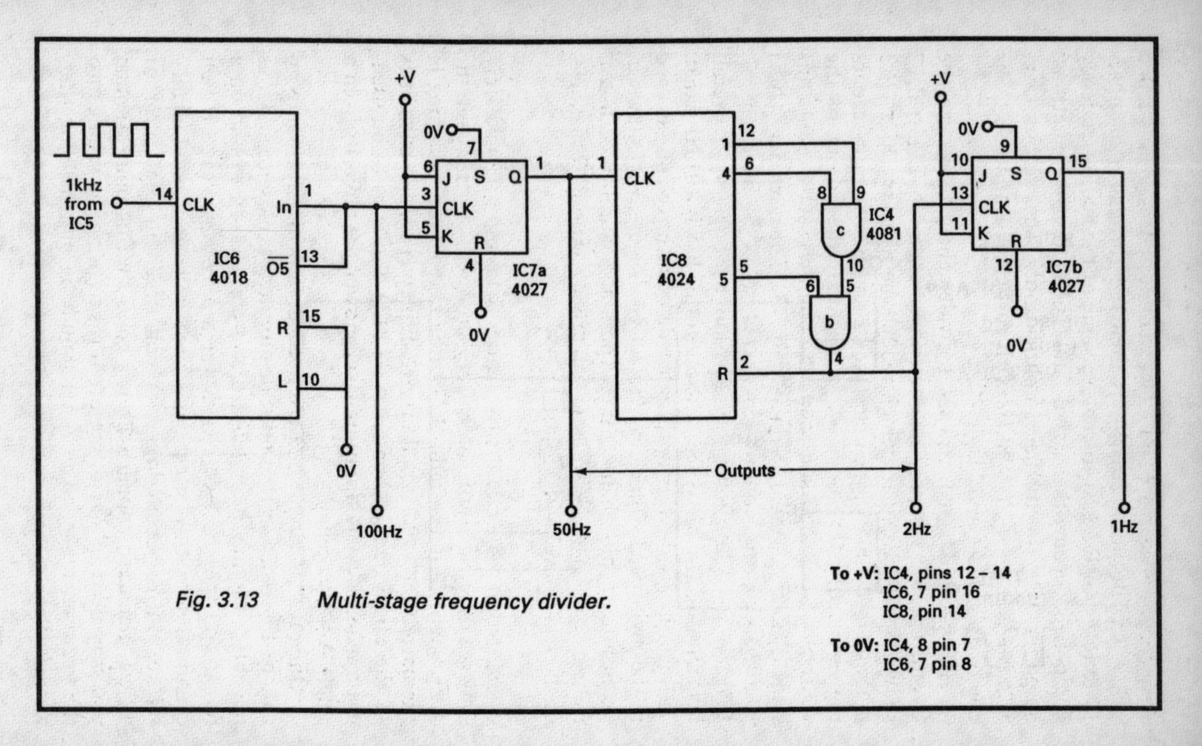

Fig. 3.13 Multi-stage frequency divider.

frequency transistors (TR1, TR2) connected as a long-tailed pair. The output from this is then fed through a high-pass filter (C7 and R7/R8) to remove some of the audio-frequency component from the signal and then to an operational amplifier IC2 for further amplification. The output from IC2 is a sine wave at 198kHz with sufficient amplitude to be compatible with CMOS logic.

All that is needed now is a divider chain to reduce the frequency of the signal to some convenient level. Figure 3.12 shows a pair of dividers which reduce the signal to 1kHz. IC3 is a binary divider tapped at stages 2 and 6. When it reaches the count of 100010 (= 34 in decimal) the output of the AND gate goes high and resets the counter. As a result, this stage divides the radio frequency by 33. The next stage (IC5) is a walking-ring counter connected so as to divide by 6. Division by 33 followed by division by 6 gives an overall division of 33 × 6 = 198. The output of IC5 is a 1kHz signal. This can be used for driving a decade counting chain, as used in the high-speed stop-clock, Project 14. Figure 3.13 shows an extension of the chain with outputs at a number of useful frequencies. This is suitable for driving various stop-clocks or the real-time clock (Project 1).

Construction: The circuits of Figures 3.11 and 3.12 take only 7mA so they can easily be battery powered. In this case, the 1.5V supply for the radio IC can be taken from a tapping in the battery box. A liquid crystal display (page 19) adds little to the power requirements. If an LED display is to be used, use a mains power supply unit and power the radio IC from a single AA type cell.

Only a small circuit board is needed, on which the components of the radio section must be mounted as close together as possible. L1 may be purchased as a coil already wound on a ferrite rod, but be sure to ask for a *long-wave* coil. If you cannot obtain this, wind your own coil on a good-quality ferrite rod 15–20cm long. A coil of about 300 turns of 40swg enamelled copper wire is a good starting point, though you may need to add or remove turns to bring the tuning into the required range. The turns should be bunched together, wound slightly criss-cross to produce a thick, compact coil.

C1 is a silvered-mica plate capacitor and C2 a variable trimmer capacitor with a range of 5 to 65pF. C3 to C6 are polyester capacitors.

Assemble the radio section first with a miniature jack socket for the earphone. The earphone is of the crystal type as used with transistor radios and tape recorders. When the 1.5V supply is connected (no need for the main 6V supply yet), adjust C2 until you hear BBC Radio 4 clearly. If the signal is weak, try turning the aerial horizontally, for the best reception is achieved from the direction perpendicular to the rod. If you have an oscilloscope, connect it across L1; a 198kHz sinusoidal waveform, with amplitude in the region of 30mV is seen. This signal is seen on the oscilloscope even when the power to the radio IC is switched off. The waveform is seen to vary in amplitude according to the audio-frequency signal with which it is modulated. If you do not have an oscilloscope to view the waveforms at each stage of the circuit, this need not prevent you from building this project; you will simply have to wait until it is complete before testing it. For those without an oscilloscope, the output from the earphone indicates if the receiver is correctly tuned.

The next stage is the differential amplifier TR1 and TR2; be sure to use radio-frequency transistors such as 2N2222A for this. With an oscilloscope, monitor the output at the junction of R6 and the collector of TR2. This is a 198kHz sinusoidal waveform of amplitude about 70mV, modulated as before. Incidentally, the volume of the sound is reduced when the radio IC is connected to TR1, as this taps off some of the signal which formerly went to the IC. There is no need to worry about this. You will also find that connecting to TR1 slightly alters the capacitance of the tuning loop so that C2 needs to be re-adjusted for maximum volume.

When you have completed the op amp stage, check the output of IC2. It is a sinusoidal waveform with 2V amplitude. The amplitude at all stages depends upon the strength of reception and on the accuracy of the tuning. If necessary, re-adjust C2 to obtain the maximum amplitude. With strong reception, the signal from IC2 may become clipped at about ±2V and approach a square wave in shape; this is perfectly acceptable by the next stage of the circuit.

If you are building the 1kHz divider of Figure 3.12, monitor its output at IC5 pin 1. This is a square-wave signal at 1kHz. You can hear this in the earphone, as a high-pitched tone in the background of the radio programme.

For lower frequencies, assemble as many as necessary of the stages shown in Figure 3.13. The 2Hz signal consists of a very short high pulse which you may find difficult to detect with an oscilloscope. It is, however, long enough to trigger a clock divider chain. If you do not use the final divide-by-two stage (IC7b), connect the unused inputs at pins 9–13 to 0V or +V.

With the receiver connected to the beginning of the divider chain of one of the clocks, compare the timing with that of a reliable crystal-controlled clock, to check that the dividing chain is properly connected and is operating correctly. There is no detectable difference over a period of many hours or even days. If there *is* any difference after a while, this is presumably due to cumulative errors in the comparison check, not in the radio-receiver clock.

Project 10 – Priority Timer

(Beginner's project)

This does not *measure* time but indicates which of two events occurs first. As shown in Figure 3.14, it responds to two push-buttons and is used to settle arguments about 'Who was first?' in quiz-games and other games in which priority is a deciding factor. There are two LEDs, one for each player or team, which are extinguished by pressing the reset button. When any one player presses their button the corresponding LED lights. After one player has pressed the button, the LED of the other player can not be made to come on.

How it works: This circuit depends upon the action of a pair of J-K flip-flops, both contained in the same IC. A J-K flip-flop is triggered by a positive-going edge applied to its clock input. What happens depends upon the state of the J and K inputs:

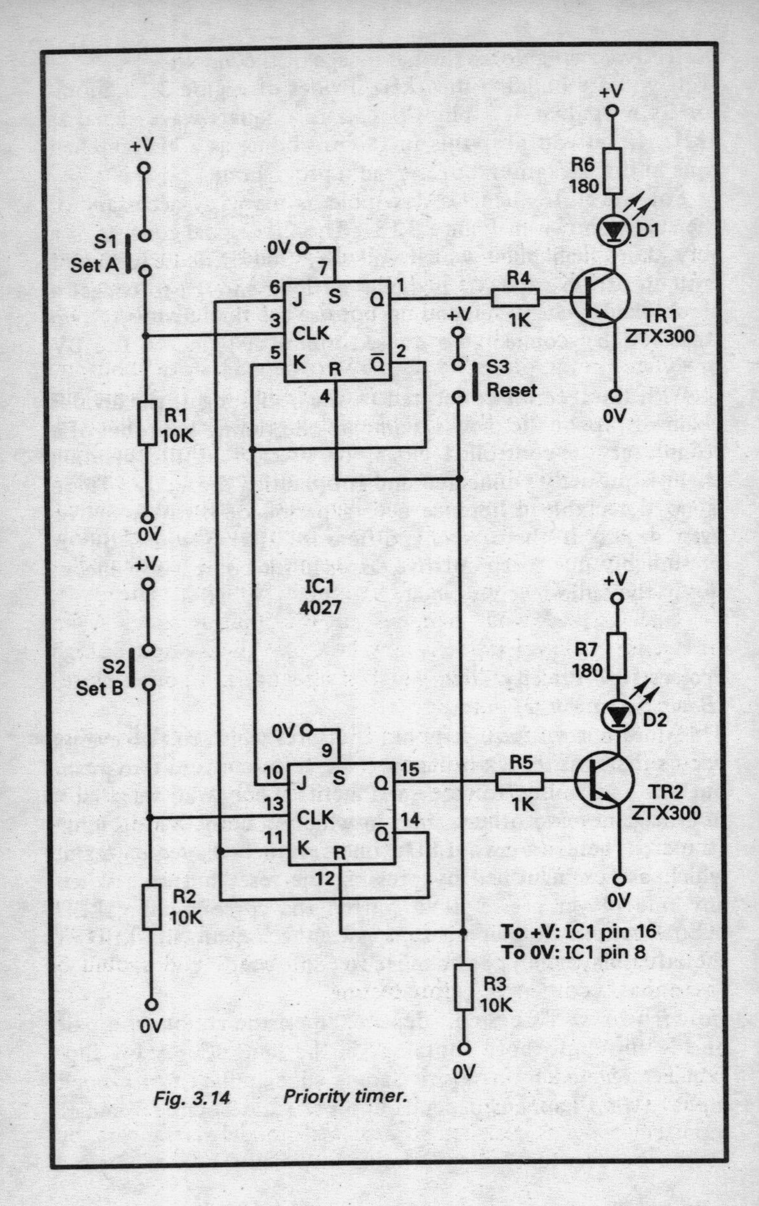

Fig. 3.14 *Priority timer.*

Inputs		Output
J	*K*	*Q*
0	0	No change
0	1	0
1	0	1
1	1	Changes

In this table 0 signifies a low voltage and 1 a high voltage. When J and K are both high the output Q changes from 0 to 1 or from 1 to 0, depending upon what it was before. The $\overline{Q}$ output is always the inverse of the Q output.

When the flip-flops are reset by pressing S3, both Q outputs go low, both transistors are turned off and both LEDs are out. Let us consider the flip-flop belonging to player A. Since the flip-flops are reset, both $\overline{Q}$ outputs are high. Both the J and K inputs of each flip-flop are high. If A presses S1, Q changes from 0 to 1, turns on TR1 and lights D1. At the same time $\overline{Q}$ (pin 2) goes low. This makes the K input of A's flip-flop low. Nothing happens if A presses S1 again, for J is high and K is low and the Q output is forced high, which it already is.

Now to see what happens to B's flip-flop after A has pressed S1. The J input is now low, and the K input is high. Pressing S2 forces Q low, which it already is. In other words, B can not make D2 turn on.

We have seen what happens if A presses first. If B presses first the opposite situation arises; D2 comes on and D1 can not be lit. Both LEDs come in if both switches are pressed at *exactly* the same time. By *exactly* we mean within a few hundred nanoseconds, so such as event can reasonably be taken as a dead heat.

Construction: The circuit runs on any voltage from 3V to 9V. It is easily built on a small piece of board and should be assembled completely before testing.

Project 11 – Lap Timer

(Average project)

The lap timer is designed for use with model racing cars, but could be adapted for any timing in which a broken beam of

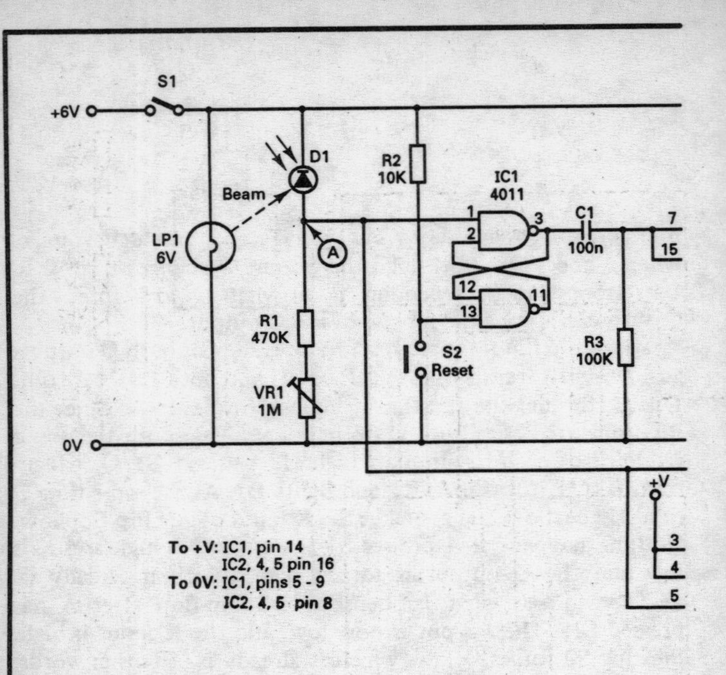

To +V: IC1, pin 14
IC2, 4, 5 pin 16
To 0V: IC1, pins 5 - 9
IC2, 4, 5 pin 8

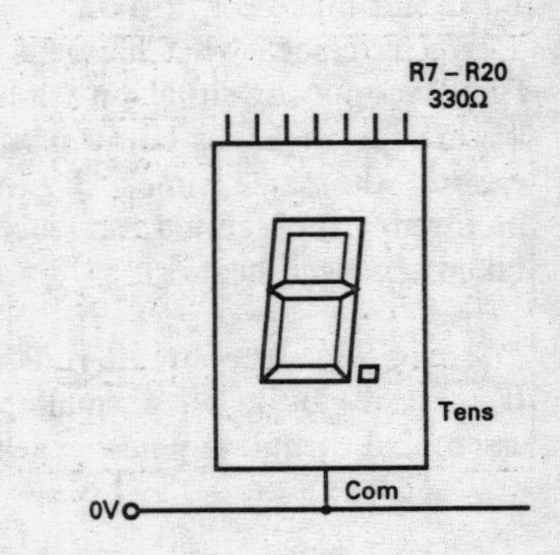

Fig. 3.15 Lap timer.

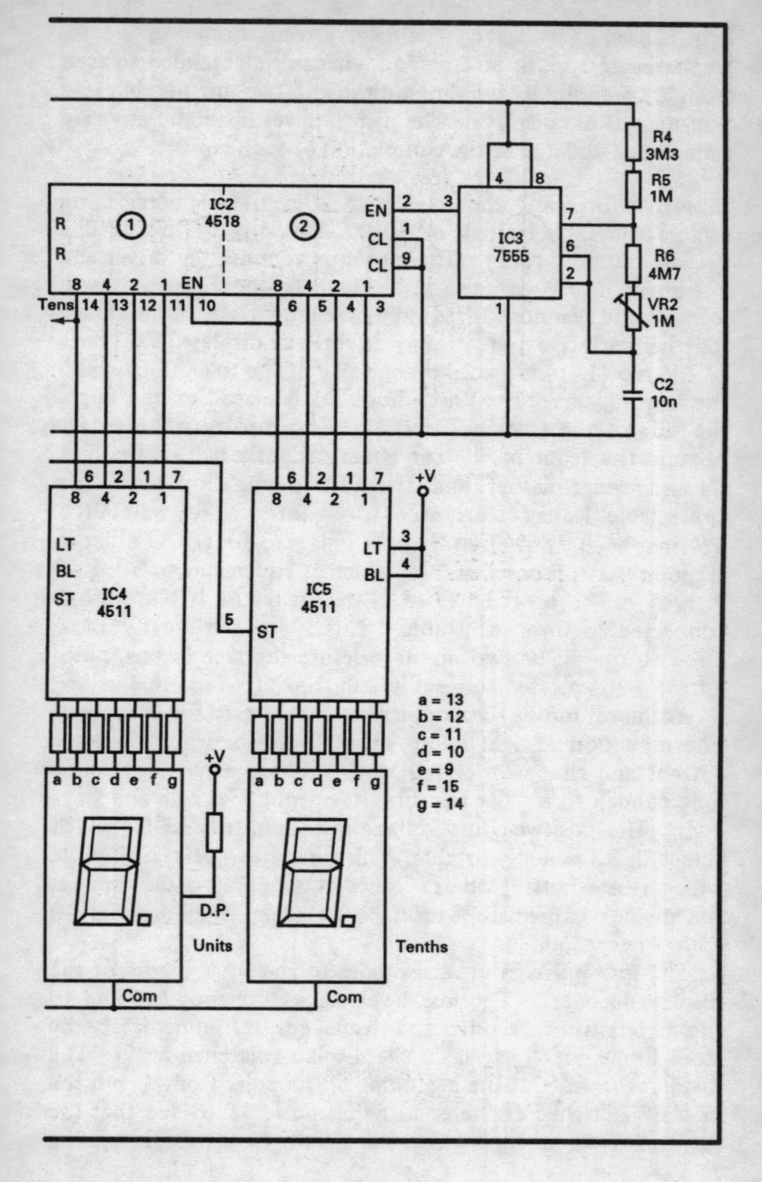
R4
3M3
R5
1M
IC2
4518
IC3
7555
R6
4M7
VR2
1M
C2
10n
R
R
EN
CL
CL
Tens
IC4
4511
IC5
4511
LT
BL
ST
+V
D.P.
Units
Tenths
Com
Com
a = 13
b = 12
c = 11
d = 10
e = 9
f = 15
g = 14

light is used as a trigger. The display reads from 0.0s to 9.9s, to the nearest tenth of a second. It can be extended to read from 0.0s to 99.9s by the addition of two further ICs and 7-segment LED displays. The display gives the cumulative lap time, being updated at the completion of each lap.

How it works: A 7555 timer (IC3, Fig. 3.15) is wired as an astable with a frequency of 10Hz. This drives two cascaded decade counters (IC2). These each have a display driver and 7-segment display connected to them to show the tenths of seconds and seconds. If required, a second divider IC is added, together with two more display drivers and displays.

A lamp (LP1) is placed on one side of the track in line with the starting line. The photodiode D1 is placed on the opposite side of the track. The beam is not broken at this stage because the front of the car is very slightly behind the line. D1 is reverse-biassed and the full illumination causes an appreciable leakage current to flow through R1 and VR1. VR1 has been adjusted so that the p.d. across R1/VR1 (that is, at point A) is more than 3V, which is equivalent to a logical high at pin 1 of IC1. Two NAND gates of IC1 are cross-connected to form a bistable. This is set or reset by a low pulse to one of its two inputs. Before the race begins, push-button S2 is pressed to reset it, and the output at pin 3 is low.

As the car moves forward, it breaks the beam for an instant. The reduction of light falling on D1 causes a drop in leakage current and thus a brief fall in the voltage at A. The fall is long enough to set the bistable. Its output goes high and stays high. The positive-going voltage is transmitted to C1 which acts with R3 as a monostable. This generates a *brief* high pulse which resets both dividers. Since this is only a short pulse, the divider immediately resumes counting at the rate of 10 counts per second.

The low pulse from A also goes to the store inputs of the display decoders. The low level allows the present input to the drivers to be decoded and displayed, but immediately the store input goes high again the display is latched again. The dividers are reset at the beginning of the pulse from A, but the display is latched at the end of that pulse. Provided that the car moves fast enough, which will usually be the case, resetting and latching occur virtually at the same time and the display then shows 0.0s.

When the car has completed one lap the beam is broken again. The bistable has remained set so there is no change in its state and the divider is not reset. But a pulse goes to the drivers which causes them to take up and latch the present count from the dividers. The display changes almost instantly to show and hold the time of the first lap. This is repeated at the completion of each lap.

Construction: Figure 3.15 shows a 6V filament lamp as the source of the beam. If preferred, this can be powered from a separate battery, or might be replaced by an electric torch or even a mains lamp, such as a table-lamp. The photodiode is any general-purpose type. Build the astable and wire up the diode. Set up the lamp. With a voltmeter check that the voltage at A is above 3V when the beam is unbroken and below 3V when it is broken, test the operation of the bistable. Pin 3 goes low when S2 is briefly pressed, and goes high when the beam is briefly broken. A photodiode has been chosen as sensor because this has a very short response time. The bistable is set even when the car passes very rapidly through the beam.

Assemble the timer circuit next. Use a polyester capacitor for C2 (10 000pF). R4 and R5 in series give 4.3MΩ, a value that is not readily obtainable as a single resistor. VR2 should be a Cermet pot for best stability. Now connect the divider (IC2), display drivers (IC4, IC5) and displays. For the present, wire the two reset inputs (pins 7 and 15) to the 0V line so that the counter runs continuously for testing. Note that the displays *must* be of the common cathode type. In this project we use series resistors (compare Project 1, page 15). It is often more convenient to use two DIL packages each containing 7 resistors. If these are not available for 330Ω, use 270Ω instead. As shown in Figure 3.15, the timer registers only up to 9.9s. If you require longer timing, and another divider IC, connect in exactly the same way as IC2, except that its input pin 2 is connected to pin 14 of IC2 (where the figure has an arrow labelled 'TENS'). This provides two more decades, timing up to 999.9s, though you need not display the 'hundreds' decade. Connect one (timing to 99.9s) or two (timing to 999.9s) driver ICs to this (exactly as for IC4 and IC5) and also one or two more displays with resistors.

When power is switched on, the display increments from zero to its maximum value repeatedly. Check that it is operating correctly. If numbers appear in the wrong sequence, check the connections between the dividers and drivers. If strange symbols appear instead of numbers (or the display is occasionally blank) check the connections between the drivers and the displays. Use a watch or clock to set VR2 so that the IC3 is running at the correct rate. This is not really practicable with only a 2-digit display. You will then have to rely on the precision of the capacitors and the adjustment of VR2. Use a precision polystyrene capacitor (±1%) for C2. Use a testmeter to measure exactly the combined resistance of R4 and R5 in series (which should be approximately 4.3MΩ). Then remove IC3 from its socket or disconnect R6 and VR2, and use a multimeter to measure their combined resistance in series. Calculate what this should be:

$$(R6 + VR2) = \frac{14.4 - (R4 + R5)}{2}$$

All resistances are expressed in megohms. Adjust VR2 until the combined resistance is as calculated.

When you are satisfied with the timing, remove the connection from 0V to IC2 pins 7 and 15. Connect these pins to C1 instead, to complete construction.

Project 12 – Low Cost Minutes Timer

(Beginner's project)

This project has only 4 ICs and, since it does not have a display, it is relatively cheap to build and simple to assemble. It has low power requirements so is very suitable as a compact battery-powered project. It gives reasonably precise timing for intervals of from 1 to 16 minutes. The timer is set by turning a switch to the SET position; a series of beeps is heard at the rate of one every second. Count the beeps until the

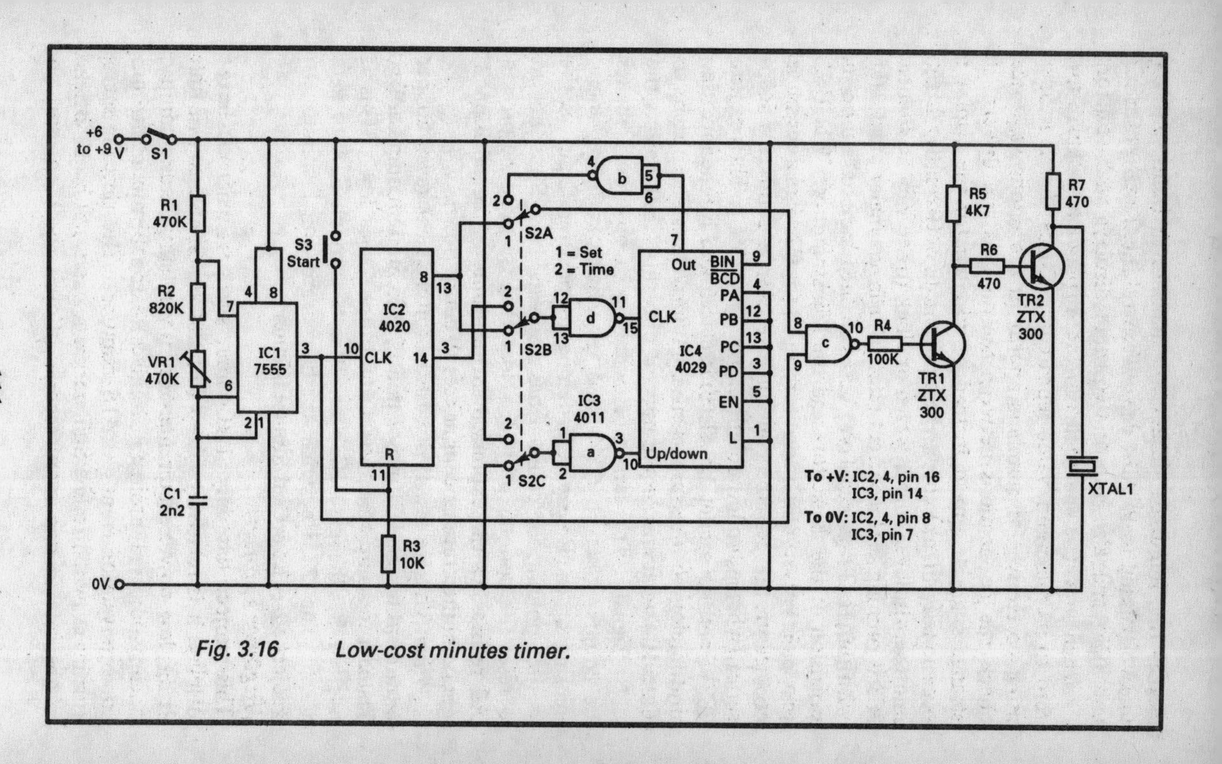

Fig. 3.16 Low-cost minutes timer.

number of beeps heard equals the number of minutes to be timed. Immediately turn the switch to the TIME position. Press the START button; timing begins as soon as the button is released. At the end of the interval the sounder is heard for a period of 1 minute.

The project has the advantages that it is easily operable in the dark or by persons with deficient eyesight.

How it works: Timing is provided by a 7555 (IC1, Fig. 3.16), running at approximately 273Hz. This frequency is divided by 2^8 and 2^{14} by IC2. The resulting frequencies are 1.1Hz and 0.167Hz (1 per minute). These frequencies are used to control IC4, which is a 4-stage up-down counter. When S2 is in position 1 (SET), S2A selects the 1.1Hz signal which is mixed with the 273Hz signal by gate IC3c to produce a beeping signal. This is amplified by TR1 and TR2 to activate the piezo-electric sounder XTAL1. S2C followed by the inverting action of gate IC3a makes the UP/DOWN control high, to cause IC4 to count in the upward direction. S2B selects the 1.1Hz signal. The action of switching to position 1 makes the counter reset to 0000, and then begin counting, incrementing at each beep. Switching to position 2 leaves the counter holding the count it has reached. Now S3 is pressed to reset the counter of IC2. Note that S3 must be pressed and released within about 30s of turning S2 to position 2, otherwise the counter commences to count down.

When S3 is released, pulses reach IC3 at the rate of 1 per minute. Since S2C is in position 2, the counter counts *down.* When it reaches zero, the OUT output goes low. This is inverted by the gate IC3b and passes through S2A to gate IC3c. The 273Hz signal is then heard for 1 minute, to indicate that the preset interval is ended.

Construction: The circuit requires only 3mA when quiescent so it can be powered by a 9V PP3 battery or a battery of four size AA or AAA cells in a battery box. For greatest stability, C1 is a polystyrene capacitor and VR1 is a Cermet multi-turn preset potentiometer. XTAL1 is a piezo-electric transducer, which must be firmly mounted on a panel or a wall of the enclosure for maximum effect.

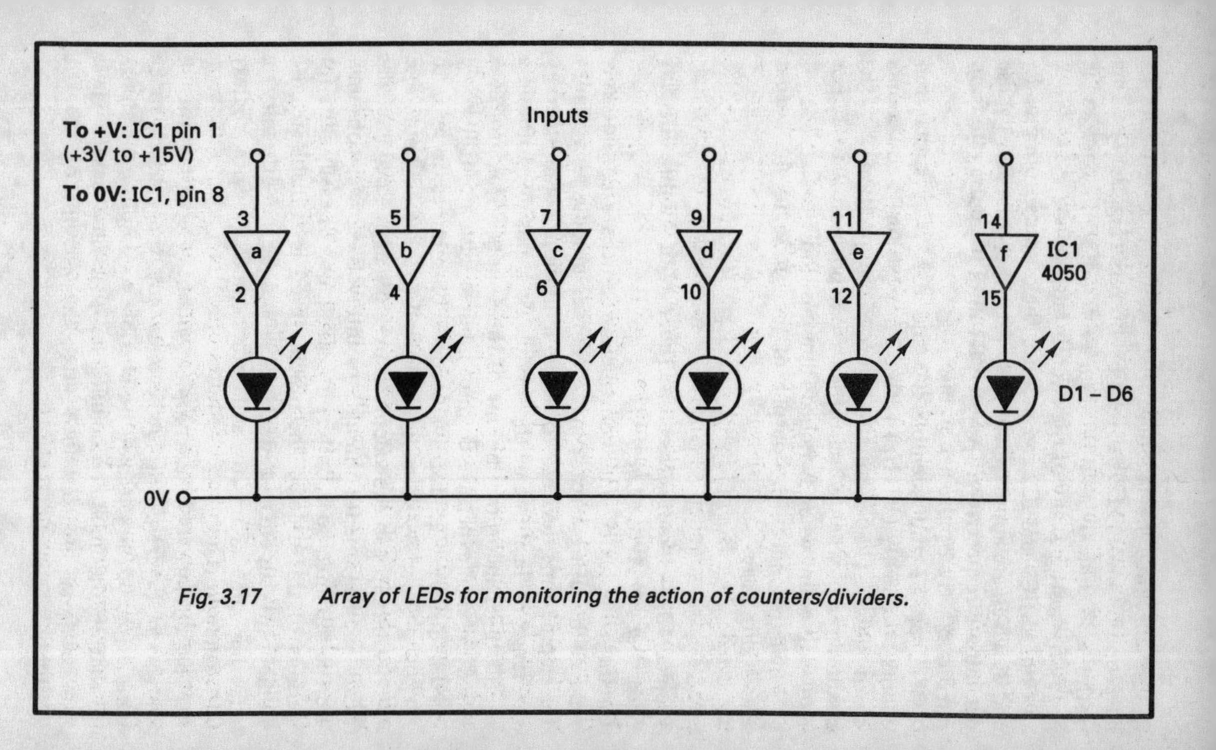

Fig. 3.17 Array of LEDs for monitoring the action of counters/dividers.

For checking the circuit during assembly, it is useful to have one or more LEDs driven by buffers (Fig. 3.17). This testing aid is quickly assembled on a scrap of strip-board and is handy for testing many of the circuits in this book.

Connect IC1 and IC2 and monitor the outputs from pins 13 and 3, which are approximately 1 pulse per second and 1 pulse per minute respectively. Adjust VR1 until the pulse rate from pin 3 is exactly 1 pulse per minute.

Wire up S3 and assemble IC3 and IC4. Check that IC4 counts up quickly (at 1Hz) with S2 in position 1, and counts down slowly (1 per minute) with S2 in position 2. The counter resets when S2 is turned from position 2 to 1, but retains its count when switched from position 1 to 2.

Finally, connect the output of gate IC3c to the output amplifying stage.

Project 13 – Minutes/Seconds Timer With Module Display
(Beginner's or Average project)

Circuit complexity and construction time are considerably reduced by using a ready-made counter module as a display for elapsed-time devices. Although limitations are imposed by the range of facilities of the module, it is possible to build a useful timer incorporating one of these units. This project is based on an inexpensive counter module with a 5-digit liquid crystal display. It displays seconds or minutes from 0 to 99 999. Since 99 999s is equivalent to over 27 hours and 99 999 minutes is equivalent to over 69 days, the timer has many applications for timing long intervals. Power consumption is minimal, so a battery of alkaline cells easily lasts for periods of this order. The module used is available from a number of suppliers and there should be no difficulty in adapting the circuit to suit other modules with slightly different features.

The circuit for the complete minutes/seconds timer is shown in Figure 3.18. A seconds-only timer has a much simpler circuit and it may be possible to simplify the circuit further if the module includes its own time base. These modifications are described after the account of the full circuit.

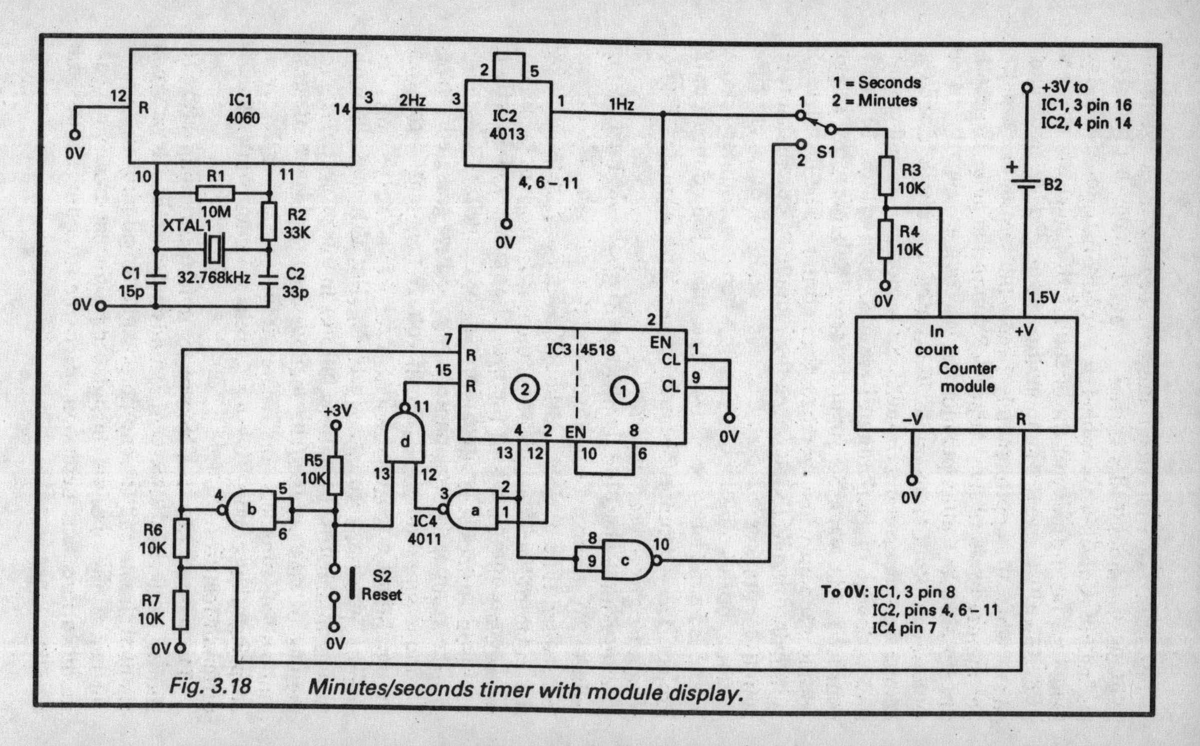

Fig. 3.18 Minutes/seconds timer with module display.

How it works: Timing relies on a quartz crystal oscillator running at 32.768Hz (page 18). This frequency is divided by 2^{14} by IC1 and further divided by 2 by IC2 to give a 1Hz signal. This is fed through S1 and a voltage-halving network (R3/R4) to the input of the module. The display increments at the rate of 1 per second. For timing minutes, the frequency is divided by 60 using IC3 connected as in Project 1, except that the arrangements for resetting are slightly different. The output from pin 13 is inverted by gate IC4c and fed to the module through S1 and R3/R4.

Counter 1 of IC3 is reset by a high level applied to pin 7; when S2 is pressed the input to gate IC4b goes low and its output goes high, so resetting the counter. The high level is also halved by R6/R7 to reset the module. Counter 2 is reset either by pressing S2 or by the "4" and "2" outputs of the counter both going high. This is when the counter reaches 6 and is immediately reset to zero, to make IC3 count from 00 to 59.

The module: The main features of the module used in this project are:

1. It is powered by a 1.5V cell.
2. There are terminals on the base plate connected directly to the negative and positive terminals of the cell.
3. The counter is incremented by a positive-going edge at its count input terminal. Input voltage here and at the reset input must not exceed 1.5V.
4. The maximum counting rate is 7Hz; this may limit the applications of the module but not in this project.
5. The counter is reset by a positive-going edge at its reset terminal.
6. The module has outputs providing a square wave signal at 512Hz and a sinusoidal signal at 32.768kHz. These are not used in Figure 3.18, and are not an essential feature for this project. However, if they are available, they may be used to simplify the circuit as explained later.
7. The module has an output for producing an audible tone when it is incremented or reset. This feature is not used in these timer projects.

Construction: A single cell providing 1.5V for powering the module is held in an integral cell compartment. A second cell connected in series with this (B2, Fig. 3.18) provides the minimum 3V required for powering the CMOS ICs.

Connect IC1 and IC2 as shown; use an oscilloscope, LED or voltmeter to monitor the output at pin 1 of IC2 and confirm that it is a 1Hz signal. Add the module to the circuit; the reset input is left unconnected at this stage. Confirm that the display increments once per second. If you require a timer for seconds only, you can omit S1 but not R3/R4. For resetting, provide a push-button to connect the reset terminal with the +V terminal of the module (*not* the +3V supply).

For a minutes and seconds timer, continue by assembling IC3 and IC4. With S1 switched to position 2, the display is incremented every minute and is reset by pressing S2.

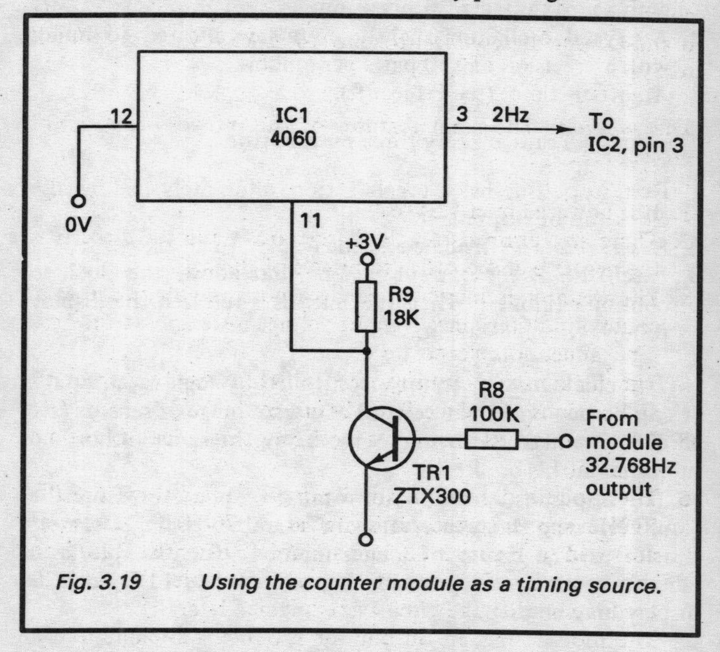

Fig. 3.19 *Using the counter module as a timing source.*

If the module has its own 32.768kHz output, this can be used as in Figure 3.19. TR1 is required to boost the signal level from the module. If the module has a 512Hz output, this can be used in a similar way. In this case, take the 1Hz output from pin 9 of IC1 and feed this directly to S1 and IC3. IC2 is not required. With a 512Hz output from the module, a seconds-only timer requires only IC1, making this a very simple project to build.

Project 14 – Stop-Clocks
(Advanced project)
Here are a set of circuits to help you to design and build a stop-clock to your own requirements.

There is a choice of time sources:

1. An astable based on the 7555 timer; the easiest to build, with approximately 2% precision.
2. A crystal oscillator; slightly more complicated to build, with a precision of ±50 parts per million.
3. An off-air timer (see Project 9).

The clock is controlled by three push-buttons:

1. Run/Stop: this has a toggle action, alternately making the clock run or stopping it.
2. Reset: resets all dividers and the display to all zeros.
3. Latch: holds the current reading, but allows the clock to continue timing. When the button is released the display follows the clock again.

The clock may instead by controlled by logic-level inputs. It can be put under the control of a wide range of sensors (see BP273, *Practical Electronic Sensors*, by the same author and publisher as this book).

The display is adaptable for a range of purposes, from the timing of very short intervals (for example, timing a camera shutter) to the timing of longer intervals (for example, as a laboratory timer, or precision lap-timer). An LED or LCD display may be used.

How it works: Two time sources are shown in Figure 3.20. The astable (page 71) in Figure 3.20a has a frequency of

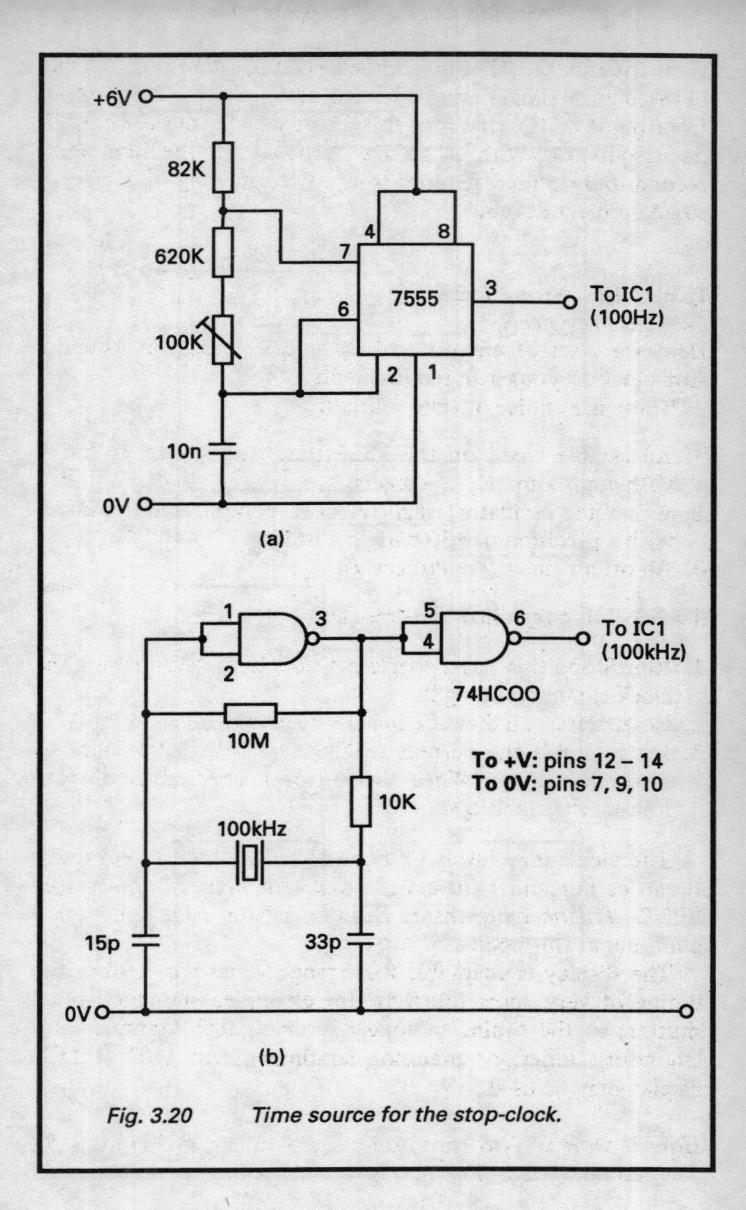

Fig. 3.20 Time source for the stop-clock.

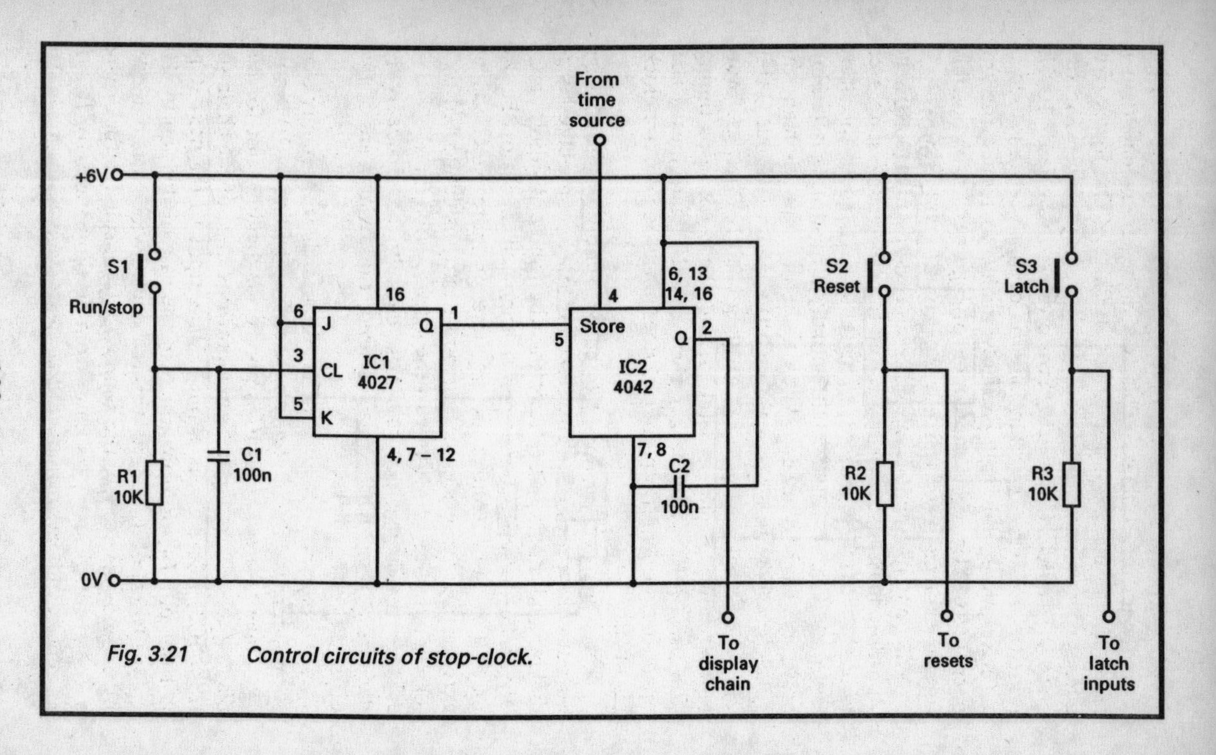

Fig. 3.21 *Control circuits of stop-clock.*

100Hz. The crystal oscillator (page 12) of Figure 3.20b has a frequency of 100kHz. This is a higher frequency than is required for many purposes, but 100kHz is the lowest frequency for which crystals are readily obtainable. The frequency is reduced by one or two dividers to 1kHz or 100Hz prior to displaying the count. If the off-air receiver is used as a time source, you will probably decide to reduce the frequency to 1kHz, using the circuit of Figure 3.12, or possibly further reducing it to 100Hz, using IC6 of Figure 3.13.

The control circuit (Fig. 3.21) consists of three parts. The Run/Stop button causes a J-K flip-flop to change state each time the button is pressed. This output is fed to the Store input of IC2. IC2 is a latch, actually a quadruple latch, but only one latch is used. When the Store input is high, the pulses from the timer pass through the latch to output Q (pin 2). They then go on to the dividing chain. When the Store input is low, Q remains latched, and the clock stops timing. The use of the latch rather than a NAND gate means that operating the Run/Stop control does not produce extra clocking pulses.

The other two buttons, S2 and S3, simply produce a high output when pressed. The reset button is connected to *all* divider and display ICs, resetting the whole dividing chain. The latch button is connected to the latch inputs of the display ICs. For control of any one or more functions by external logic, replace the button or buttons connected by a logic input, direct to IC1 or to the reset or latch lines.

The dividing chain consists entirely of divide-by-ten dividers. If an LED display is used, the dividers are of two different types:

4518 (see Fig. 3.22a): this is a dual divider, normally used for dividing by 100, but can be used for dividing by 10 if only one stage is used. This IC is purely for dividing, not for displaying digits. Its input from a previous stage of the chain (or from IC2, Fig. 3.21) is at pin 1. Its output to the next stage is from pin 14, or from pin 6 in the case of division by 10.

40110 (see Fig. 3.22b): this is a single divider which divides by 10 and also decodes the count in a form suitable for driving a 7-segment display. Its input from previous stages (or IC2) is at pin 9 and its output to the next stage is from pin 10.

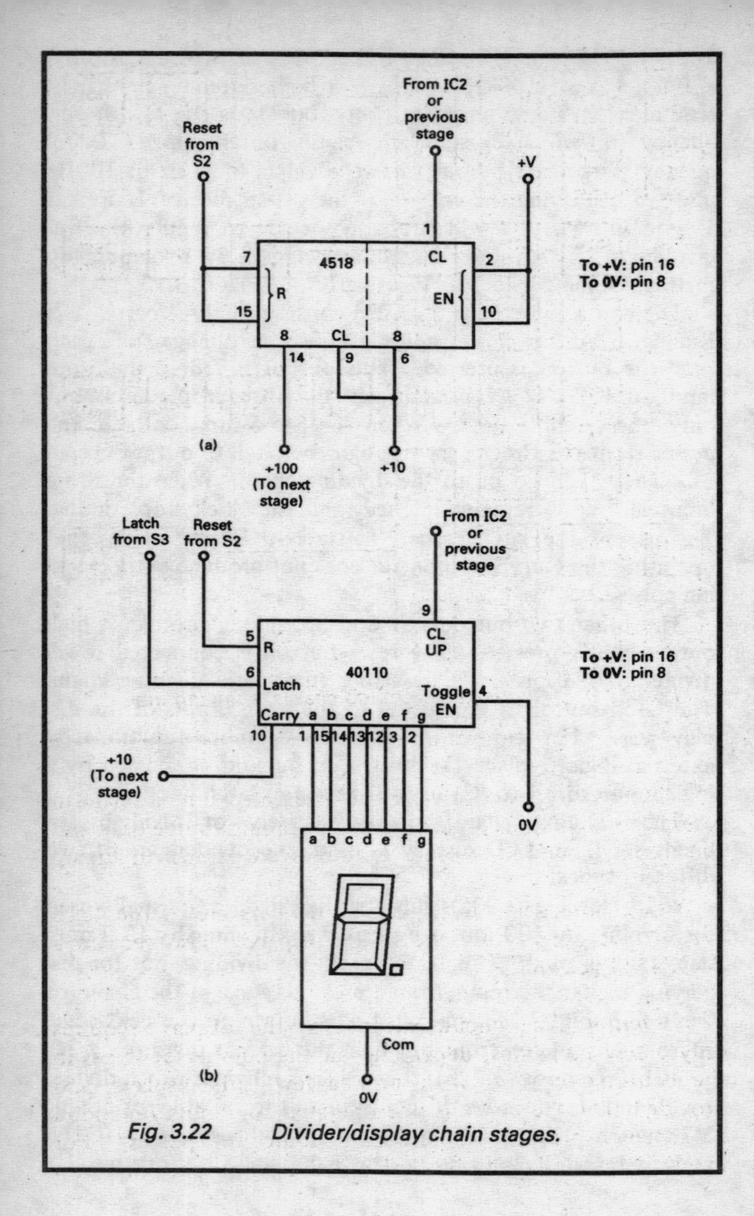

Fig. 3.22 Divider/display chain stages.

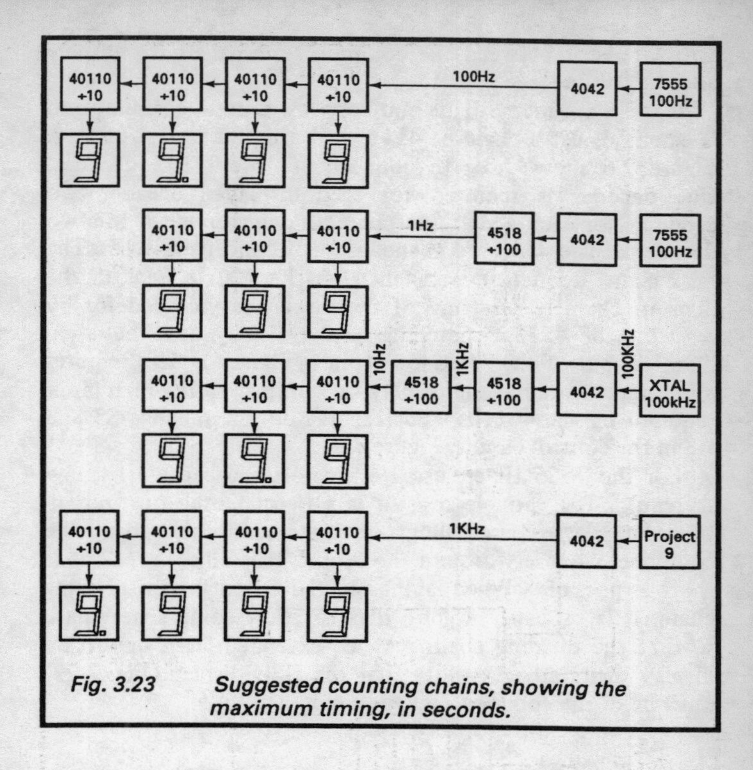

Fig. 3.23 ***Suggested counting chains, showing the maximum timing, in seconds.***

These two types of divider are assembled into a chain in various combinations according to the timing source used and the display required. Some examples are shown in Figure 3.23.

With a liquid crystal display, all dividers are of the 4518 type. The stages that are to be displayed also require a 74HC4543 decoder.

Construction: The circuit except for the display, requires only a few milliamps, depending on the number of stages in the counting chain. With only a few LED displays, and provided that the clock is not operated for hours on end, a 6V battery provides a convenient source of power. For longer periods of operation, use a mains power pack or wire a

150Ω resistor between the common terminal of the display and the 0V line (see page 136).

If there are many digits and very low current consumption is essential, use a chain of 4518s and a liquid crystal display. Figure 2.6 shows how to connect the 74HC4543 decoder. One decoder is required for each displayed decade, two decoders for each 4518. Output pin connections for the two decades of the 4518 are as shown for IC2 in Figure 3.15. The back-plane frequency is taken from the 100Hz stage in the division chain. Resetting of the display is provided for by resetting the 4518s. Latching of the display uses the latch-disable input of the 74HC4543 (pin 1, Fig. 2.6). This requires a low input to latch the display, in contrast to the high input required by the 40110s. For this reason, interchange S3 and R3 in the control circuit, Figure 3.21.

For the 7555 timer, use 1% resistors and capacitor (polystyrene). The variable resistor is a Cermet multiturn potentiometer. When assembling the crystal oscillator, group the components closely around the IC and keep all connections as short as possible. When laying out the board for the dividing chain, it is probably a good idea to allow some spare space so that the dividing chain may be extended later, or further display digits added. Note that the LED display (Fig. 3.22) must be of the common cathode type.

Project 15 – Metronome

(Average project)

A device for beating time is an essential aid to practising a musical instrument. Even though that popular instrument, the electronic keyboard, may have an LED to mark the beat, and a sophisticated rhythm accompaniment, the LED usually does not distinguish the beginning of each bar, and the intricacies of the rhythm accompaniment are distracting rather than helpful. This metronome indicates the beat by a flashing LED and a regular clicking sound. The beat at the beginning of each bar is emphasised by a second LED and a discreet 'pip'.

How it works: Timing is derived from an astable, based on the 7555 timer IC (IC1, Fig. 3.24). This has a variable resistor in the charging network so that the tempo is variable over a wide range from adagio to allegro. The resistors are chosen to give a long high pulse with a very short interval; this waveform is inverted by the buffer gate (IC4a) to generate a brief flash from the LED (D1) to indicate each beat.

The output from the timer also goes to IC2, which is a walking-ring counter, programmable to divide by any number from 2 to 10. This is achieved for even divisions by selecting a given output and feeding it back to the input IN. For example, feeding back $\overline{O3}$ makes the counter divide by 6, suitable for indicating 6/8 time. For odd divisions, two of the outputs have to be ANDed together, before being fed back to the input. As an example, $\overline{O1}$ and $\overline{O2}$ are ANDed (by IC3a) to make the IC divide by 3, for indicating 3/4 time. S1 allows for division by 2, 3, 4, 6, 8, and 9, so that all the familiar time signatures are catered for, including 2/4, 3/4, 4/4, 6/8, and 9/16. The output signal from this divider is a succession of high pulses with equally long intervals between them. The pulse generator (IC5) produces a short low-going pulse each time the output from IC2 goes high. This is inverted by IC4f to a short high pulse which flashes D2, indicating the first beat of each bar.

The beat sound is generated by a short high pulse from IC4b, in synchrony with the flashing of D1. This is transmitted through C3 and R6 to the operational amplifier IC6. The amplified output of this is tapped from VR2, which acts as a volume control. It then goes to a second amplifying circuit based on TR1. IC6 acts not only as an amplifier but also as a mixer. The pulses from IC5 are inverted by IC4c, then mixed with a 1.7kHz signal from the oscillator IC4d/e, by the gate IC5c. This is then inverted by IC5b and fed to the input of the mixer amplifier by way of C4 and R7. The sound is heard as a short high-pitched 'pip' coincident with the bar-marking flash from D2.

Construction: The circuit requires less than 15mA so can be battery powered and housed in a compact case. It runs on 6V or 9V. The panel of the case requires space for mounting the controls: On/Off switch (not shown in Figure 3.24), VR1 (Tempo), S1 (Time signature, beats per bar), and VR2

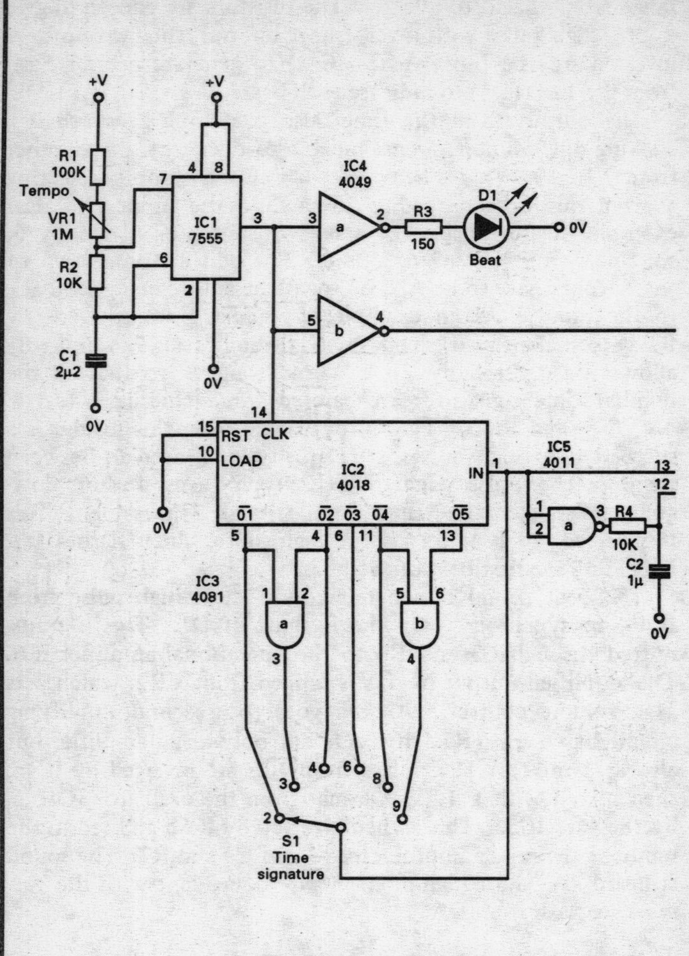

Fig. 3.24 Metronome.

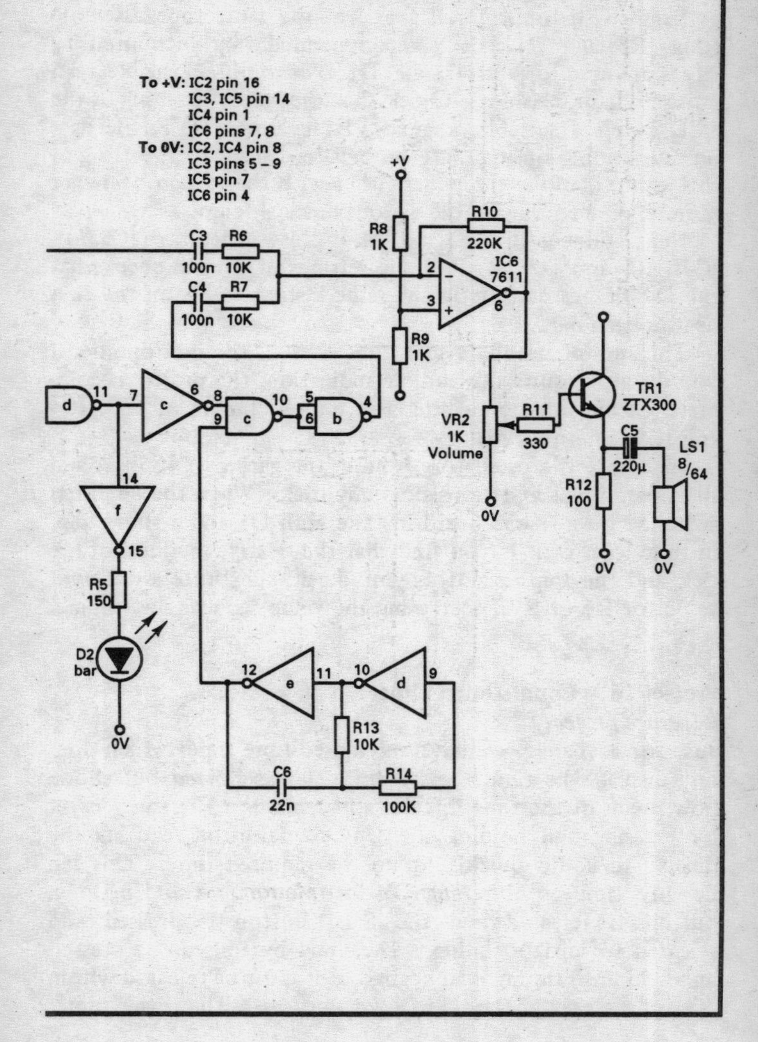

To +V: IC2 pin 16
IC3, IC5 pin 14
IC4 pin 1
IC6 pins 7, 8
To 0V: IC2, IC4 pin 8
IC3 pins 5 – 9
IC5 pin 7
IC6 pin 4
+V
R8
1K
R10
220K
C3
100n
R6
10K
C4
100n
R7
10K
IC6
7611
R9
1K
TR1
ZTX300
VR2
1K
Volume
R11
330
C5
220µ
LS1
8/64
R12
100
0V
R5
150
D2
bar
R13
10K
C6
22n
R14
100K

(Volume). It also requires space for the two LEDs (best mounted close together) and the speaker. A 38mm miniature speaker is suitable and this can have any resistance in the range 8Ω to 64Ω.

Begin with the timer IC1 and at the same time assemble IC4a, R3 and D1. It is recommended that high-intensity LEDs are used for both D1 and D2 so as to obtain the clearest, most brilliant, flashing. Check that the rate of flashing of the LED covers a suitable range as VR1 is altered. VR1 needs a pointer knob; you may later intend to calibrate the setting of this knob, marking the panel either with the rate in beats per minute, or according to the various musical tempi.

Next connect IC2, S1, IC3, the pulse generator (IC5a/d), IC4f, R5 and D2. Try all the settings of S1 and check that the D2 flashes at exactly the same instant as D1 on the first beat of each bar.

This completes the visual indicators of the metronome; if you do not require the audible indication, the project is complete except for connecting the unused inputs of IC3, IC4 and IC5 either to 0V or +V.

Assemble the oscillator, IC4d/e, the gating of IC5b/c, and the operational and transistor amplifier. When the circuit is switched on a tick is heard in time with D1 and a short 'pip' in time with D2. If you find that the relative loudness of the tick and the 'pip' is not as you like it, substitute a different value for R6 or R7. Increasing the value reduces the volume.

Project 16 – Count Down Timer

(Average project)

Just for a change, we have an elapsed-time timer which does not display the time elapsed since it was *started* but shows how much of the time interval still *remains*. The timer is set by pressing and holding the Up/Down button, causing the display to count quickly up to the required time. This can be any time in the range 0–99 minutes. The Up/Down button is released and the Start button is pressed and released to initiate timing. The Start button can be pressed and held until timing is to begin, but it must be released within 30s of releasing the Up/Down button. Then the timer commences to count down, decrementing the display once every minute. It emits a bleep at the end of every 10 minutes.

If you prefer a simpler circuit, the second counter and display is omitted to give a 0–9 minute timer, which is perfectly adequate for many purposes. If you do not require the bleeping function, this can be omitted, as explained later.

How it works: The project requires two time sources so we use a 7556 dual timer IC. One of the timers is wired as an astable (Fig. 3.25) to generate the basic timing frequency of 546Hz. This also doubles as the frequency of the bleep. A 14-stage divider, IC2 reduces the frequency to approximately 4Hz at pin 6, and to 1 pulse every 30s at pin 3. These two frequencies are halved again by IC3. This is a dual J-K flip-flop. The flip-flop not only halves the frequencies but allows either one or the other, *but not both*, to be passed to the first counter/decoder stage IC4.

When S2 is not pressed, the J-K inputs of flip-flop 1 are low and the output Q of this flip-flop remains latched, either high or low. But the J-K inputs of flip-flop 2 are high, so the Q output of this flip-flop alternates between high and low once per minute. This signal goes to the Clock Down input of the counter. This is used for counting down the required interval.

The situation is reversed when S2 is pressed. The Clock Down input is held high or low and a 2Hz alternating input goes to the Clock Up input of the counter. It increments its count twice per second. This is used for the initial setting of the timer.

In order that the first count down takes place exactly 1 minute after the timer is started, all counters must be reset after the display has been set to the required time. Pressing the Start button resets IC2 to all zeros. However, IC3 is clocked by a *positive-going* edge, so the output from pin 3 of IC2 must be inverted (by IC6d) so that IC3 receives a high input on resetting. This goes low after 30s and high again after 1 minute, clocking the second flip-flop of IC3 to change state at the correct instant. For fast upward counting, it does not matter at exactly what moment the first clocking pulse arrives, so there is no need to invert the output from pin 6 of IC2.

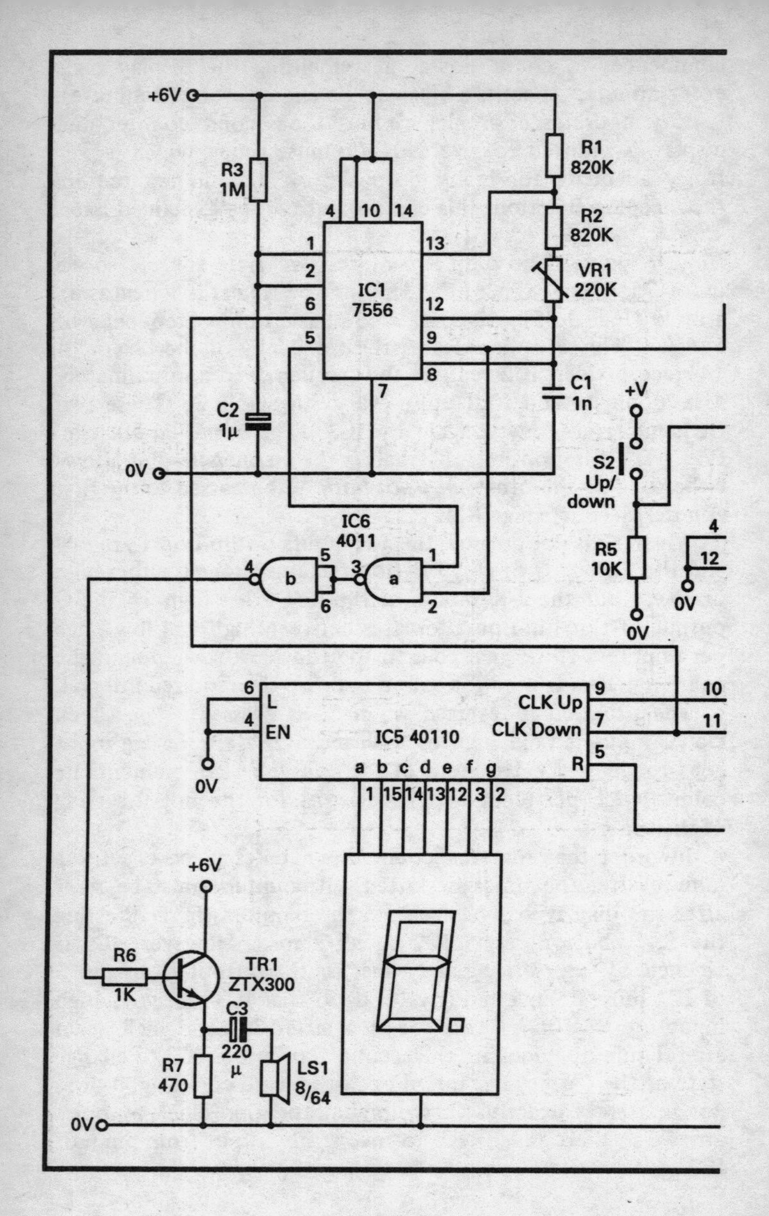

+6V
R3
1M
4
10
14
R1
820K
R2
820K
1
13
2
IC1
7556
VR1
220K
6
12
5
9
8
7
C1
1n
C2
1μ
+V
0V
S2
Up/
down
IC6
4011
4
12
R5
10K
0V
0V
4
b
5
3
a
1
6
2
6
L
9
CLK Up
10
4
EN
IC5 40110
CLK Down
7
11
5
R
0V
a b c d e f g
1 15 14 13 12 3 2
+6V
R6
1K
TR1
ZTX300
C3
220
μ
R7
470
LS1
8/64
0V

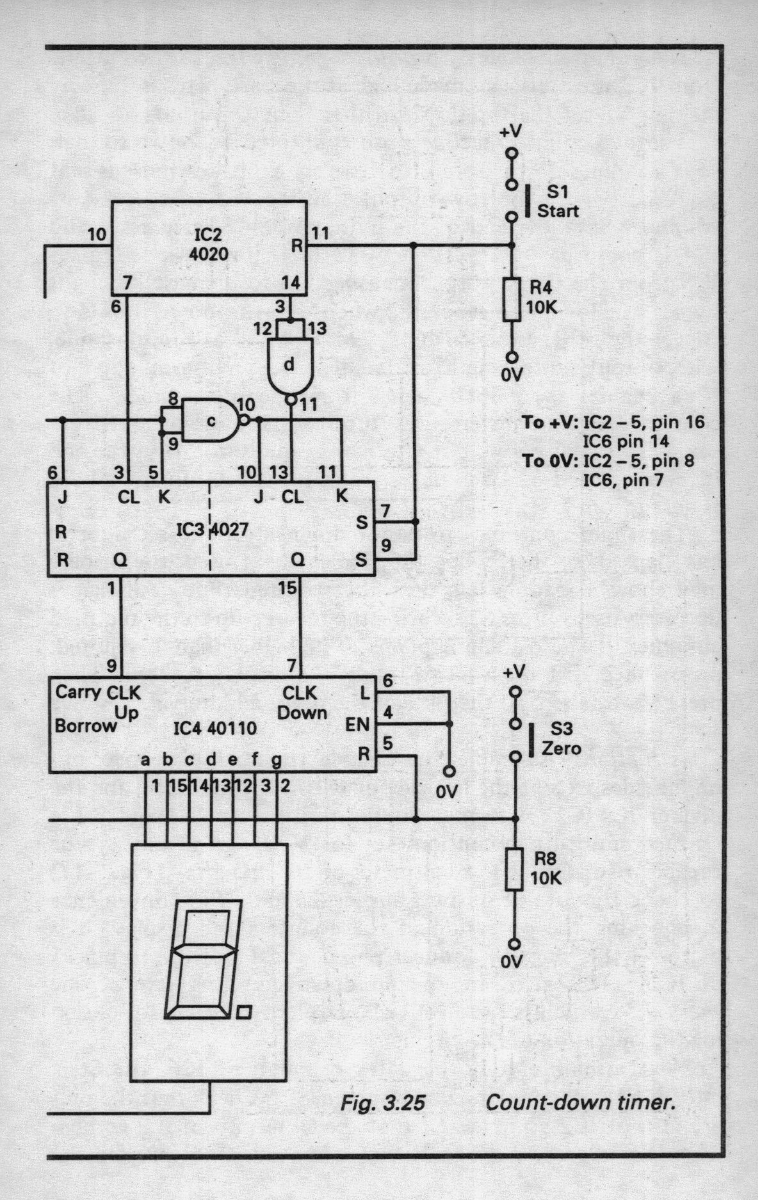

Fig. 3.25 Count-down timer.

IC4 is also clocked by a *positive-going* edge, so the outputs from IC3 must also be made high at the start. This is done by making S1 *set* the flip-flops, so that their Q outputs go high.

The two counter/decoders are connected as shown so that, as IC4 counts down from 0 to 9, a very short low pulse is sent to IC5 from the Borrow output, causing IC5 to decrease its count by 1 at the end of the pulse. When S2 is pressed and IC4 is counting up from 9 to 0, a brief low pulse is sent to IC5 from the Carry output, causing IC5 to increase its count by 1. The low pulse generated when counting down is used to trigger the other timer in IC1. This is wired as a monostable, with output pulse length of 1s. The high pulse at pin 1 of IC6a enables the 546Hz signal from the other timer. The combined signal is inverted by IC6b, so that the output from pin 4 is normally low, but alternates rapidly for 1s at the end of every period of 10 minutes. This turns TR1 on and a beep is heard from LS1.

The timer continues to count down after the set interval has elapsed, so that, when the timer is next used, the display may show a reading less than the required time. All that is necessary is to press S2 to bring the reading up to the required amount. If the reading happens to be higher than is required, press the Zero button S3 to return the display to zero. Then press S2 to take it to the time of the required interval.

Construction: Assemble the astable timer (the connections on all sides except the left side of IC1 in Figure 3.25), and the divider IC, IC2. Use metal-oxide resistors for R1 and R2, a Cermet multiturn potentiometer for VR1 and a polystyrene capacitor for C1. Use a voltmeter or an LED array (Fig. 3.17) to check the rate of outputs at pins 6 and 3. For convenience in checking the operation of the counters and display, it is better at this stage to connect pins 3 and 13 of IC3 to pin 15 of IC2. This gives an up and down counting rate of one every 7.5s which is faster but allows plenty of time for checking the operation of the circuit.

Next assemble IC3, the gates c and d of IC6, the Start button S1, and the Up-Down button S2. Check that the pins 3 and 6 of IC2 go low, and that the Q outputs of IC3 go high when S1 is pressed. Check that when S2 is not pressed the output at pin 15 of IC3 alternates between high and low, but that at pin 1 remains constant. The situation is reversed when S2 is pressed.

Wire up IC5, IC6, S3 and the displays. Note that the displays must be of the common cathode type. No series resistors are required with a 6V power supply. Confirm that the counters operate correctly, counting up with S2 not pressed, down with S2 pressed, and resetting to 00 when S3 is pressed.

Connect gates a and b of IC6, assemble the second timer (R3, C2), and the amplifier and speaker. Any speaker in the range 8Ω to 64Ω can be used. Reset the display to 00; a 1s beep is heard as the display changes to 99.

Finally, make the correct connection between IC2 and IC3 as shown in the figure. Press S3. Press S2 to set a reading of a few minutes. Press S1 and, as you release it note the time on a seconds watch or clock. Adjust VR1 as necessary so that the timer changes exactly on the minutes.

For a 1–9 minute timer, simply omit IC5 and its LED display. With only 1 digit, it is not necessary to provide for resetting to zero; omit S3 and R8, and connect pin 5 of IC4 directly to 0V.

If you decide to dispense with the audible warning, it is best to substitute a single 7555 timer for IC1. Connect this as shown in Figure 3.20a, but with the component values of Figure 3.25. The amplifier and loudspeaker are not required. Gates a and b of IC6 are not used and their input pins (1, 2, 5, 6) must be connected either to +V or 0V.

Project 17 – Simple Precision Timer

(Beginner's project)

Based on only two integrated circuits, this is a very good "first project" for the beginner. Yet it is capable of timing with a precision of 0.01% (6ms per minute). Taking into account temperature variations, its timing varies by only about 0.25s per minute for a change in temperature of 10°C. The timer has a single LED digit which displays zero when the timer is first switched on. This increments at the rate of 1 count per minute. The circuit is adaptable for timing for periods of other lengths such as seconds, hours or days. In

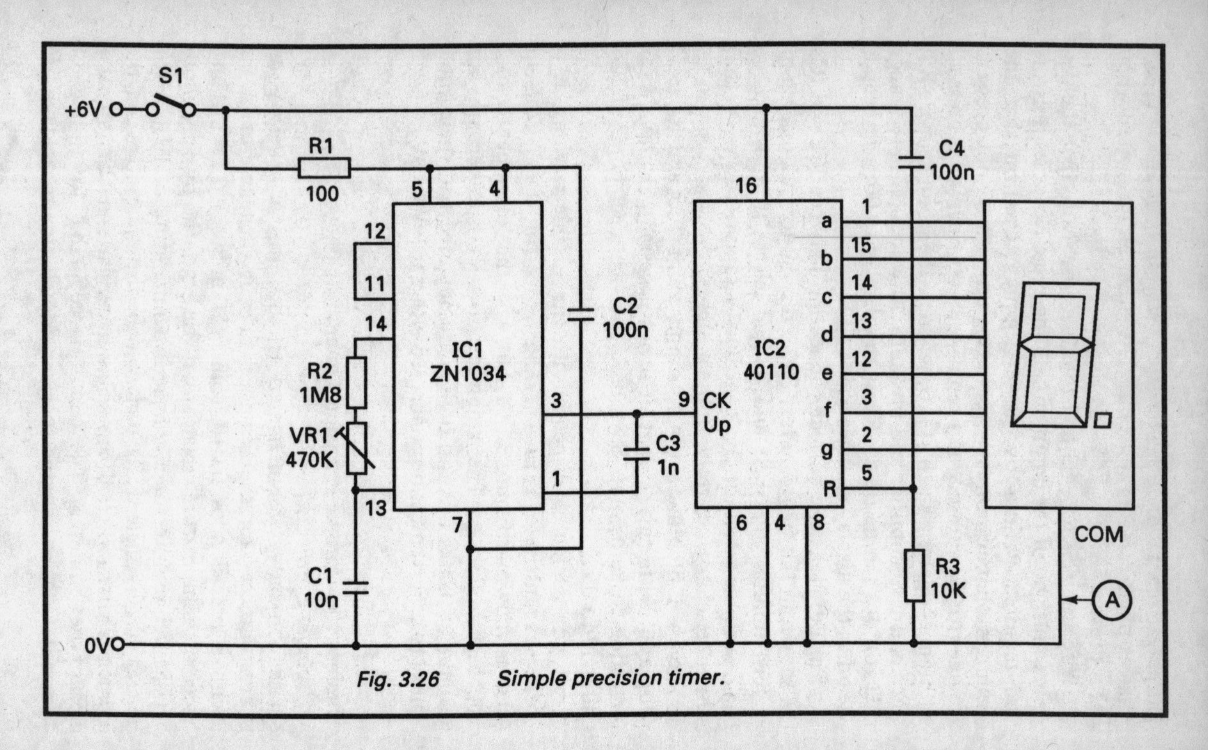

Fig. 3.26 Simple precision timer.

the latter form it would make a simple day-of-the-month indicator.

How it works: Timing is provided by the ZN1034 precision timer IC which includes an oscillator circuit, a 12-stage dividing chain and an internal voltage reference, to ensure reliability of operation. Because of the divider, it is possible to time relatively long periods while using a low-value capacitor. We use the very stable and precise polystyrene capacitors, available only in values up to 10nF. The timing resistance is R2 and VR1 in series; C1 is the timing capacitor. The values shown in Figure 3.26 allow the timing to be adjusted for an interval of 1 minute. The timer is triggered into operation by a low pulse applied to pin 1.

The output from pin 3 is high during timing and goes low at the end of the period. This negative-going edge is transmitted through C3 to pin 1, triggering the timer to repeat the timing cycle indefinitely.

Timing is initiated by switching on the power supply (S1), and begins from that instant. At power-up, C4 is uncharged, pulling the reset input of IC2 high, causing the counter to be reset to zero. The result is that the display shows zero when the timer is switched on. Then C4 gradually charges through R3, and the reset input falls to 0V. Thus the counter is ready to receive the first pulse from IC1 when it arrives almost 1 minute later. To reset the timer, switch off, then switch on again.

Construction: This is a very compact circuit, needing a board about 6cm by 3cm, including room for the display. As a beginner's project it is advisable to mount the ICs and the display in sockets, so that the ICs and display can be inserted *after* the soldering has been done and the connections checked. Special sockets are available for ICs, but none are available for LED displays. Usually, displays have the pins along the top and bottom edges, or along the left and right sides, spaced 2.54mm apart. A socket is made up by using two rows of IC socket strip. This has sockets mounted 2.54mm apart in a strip of plastic. The plastic is snapped off to give a strip with the required number of sockets. Another version (Soldercon) has sockets connected by a metal strip. The strip is broken off after the sockets have been soldered to the circuit board.

If the display is run at maximum brightness, the circuit requires about 350mA. A battery of four AAA alkaline cells lasts about 3 hours; a battery of four AA cells lasts about twice as long. Considerable saving of current is achieved by wiring a 150Ω resistor between the common terminal of the display and the 0V line (point A in Figure 3.26). The display is dimmer, but still clearly visible, while the current requirement is reduced to only 20mA. Now a battery of four AA cells lasts nearly 50 hours. With reduced brightness, it becomes feasible to use zinc-air button cells to make the timer really compact. Four of type A675 last for 20 hours.

For highest precision and reliability, use a metal film resistor for R2 and a Cermet multiturn potentiometer for VR1. C1 should be a polystyrene capacitor (10nF = 10 000 pF). The display unit is of the common cathode type. S1 can be an ordinary SPST toggle switch, though you may prefer to install a latching (push-on/push-off) switch.

It is best to assemble the whole circuit before testing it. To shorten testing time, use a 220kΩ resistor in place of R2 and VR1. The timer increments every 6s and correct action can be quickly checked. If irregular numerals appear on the display, check the connections between IC2 and the display. Then wire in R2 and VR1. Adjust VR1 until the display changes exactly on each minute.

As connected in Figure 3.26 the display counts up. If you would like it to count down instead, connect pin 3 of IC1 to pin 7 of IC2 instead of to pin 9. You could wire in a switch to select either pin 7 or 9, giving the timer both up and down actions.

Other timing regimes: If high precision is not important, use a 2.2MΩ resistor, 1% or 2% tolerance, in place of both R2 and VR1. The capacitor will probably already have 1% tolerance. The timing interval will then be 60.17s, which is certainly close enough to 1 minute for timing processes such as boiling an egg.

The equation for the timing interval is:

$$t = 2735RC$$

where t is in seconds, R is in ohms and C is in farads. The table below gives suitable values for other periods of timing:

Interval	*R*	*C*
10 minutes	2.2MΩ	100nF
1 hour	1.3MΩ	1μF
1 day	3.1MΩ	10μF

For precise timing, make up the resistance from a fixed resistor and a variable resistor, as in Figure 3.26. A polycarbonate capacitor is used for C1. Note that the tolerance of this type of capacitor is usually ±20%, so that VR1 must be greater in value relative to R2, so as to allow room to adjust the timing. Once adjusted, the stability is good.

Project 18 – Relay Delay Timer
(Beginner's or Advanced project)
This circuit turns on a relay for a given period of time, allowing a wide range of electrically powered devices to be controlled. We list some examples later, but first should explain why this is designated as a Beginner's or an Advanced project. Its status depends on what type of device is to be controlled. If the switched device is powered by a low-voltage supply (say 24V or less), this project is an easy and safe one for the beginner. However, relays are especially useful for controlling mains-powered devices, and:

IF THE PROJECT IS TO BE USED FOR SWITCHING MAINS CURRENTS, IT IS UNSUITABLE FOR BEGINNERS

The circuit has a simple action. In its most basic form, pressing the button energises the relay for a period selected by switching S2 and adjusting VR1. The relay switches on the power to the controlled device, which then runs for the selected period. At the end of the period the relay is de-energised and the device is turned off. It is possible to invert the action. The device may be switched *off* for the period, and come on again at the *end*.

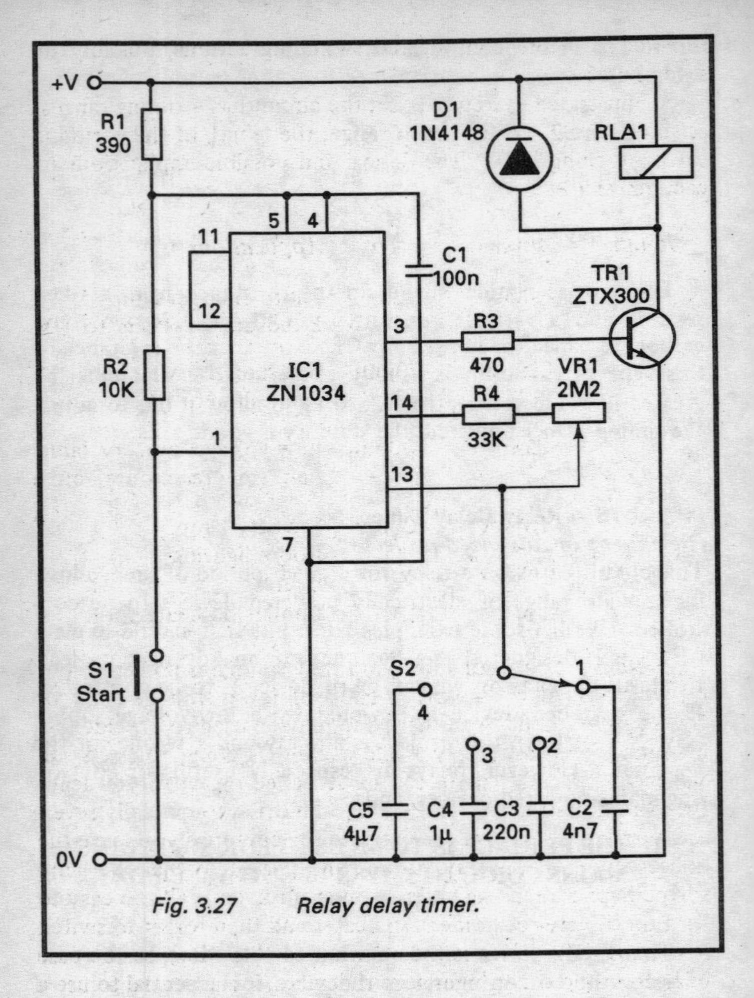

Fig. 3.27 Relay delay timer.

The advantage of using a relay is that it switches a wide range of voltages and currents. It can switch low voltages or high ones; it can switch small currents or large ones; it can switch direct current or alternating current. Certain types of relay have several sets of contacts, some of which close and some of which open when the coil is energised. These types provide for quite complicated switching actions, possibly of several devices.

As illustrated in Figure 3.27, the circuit has 4 timing ranges, selected by S2. Within each range, the length of the period is set by turning VR1. The details and possible applications of each range are:

Range	*From*	*To*	*Applications*
1	0.5s	25s	Photo-enlarger lamp Exposure of PCBs to UV
2	0.5min	20min	Corridor/stairway light Panic siren or bell
3	2min	100min	Low-voltage nursery lamp Fan (in greenhouse, etc.)
4	10min	400min	Security lamp Room lighting Heater Immersion heater.

In Range 2, the corridor lamp may be mains-powered, but to avoid use of the mains, a lamp of lower voltage (12V or 24V) can be used. A similar lamp may be used to provide low illumination in a nursery while a child is going to sleep. In Range 4, a security lamp can be switched on when you leave the house unattended, and will switch off automatically several hours later. Or you can activate the circuit as you leave the house earlier in the day, timing the period so that the lamp (or perhaps a radio set) comes on at dusk. It is all too easy to turn on a heater or immersion heater and then forget to switch it off. A delay relay is the solution to this. But, in the case of heaters and other high-current devices, it is essential to use a relay rated to withstand the high current involved. It is also very important to ensure that there is no way in which the heater can be turned on accidentally, with possible risk of fire.

How it works: Pressing S1 triggers the timer and its output at pin 3 goes high. This turns on TR1, which energises the relay coil. The time for which pin 3 is high depends on the resistance of R4/VR1 in series, and on which of C2–C5 is selected. The formula is given on page 136.

The reverse action is obtained by connecting R3 to pin 2 instead of to pin 3. D1 is present to short-circuit the back emf generated as the relay is switched off, and so protect the transistor from damage. Some types of relay have a diode built in, and D1 is not then required.

Construction: As shown, the circuit provides precise timing over all four ranges. If the circuit is to be built as a general-purpose delay switch, house it in a box with a panel large enough to mount S1, S2, VR1 and terminals wired to the contacts of the relay. Most relays have at least one set of change-over contacts, so a minimum of three terminals is required. Choose a relay that handles the largest current and highest voltage that you need. Take care never to exceed these ratings, otherwise the contacts may become damaged and fuse together.

It is possible to simplify construction if certain ranges are not required. If the delay is being built for one special application with a single time period, use the equation to calculate the value of the resistor R4 and potentiometer VR1 required. If an exact period is not essential, simply replace R4 and VR1 with a single fixed resistor of suitable value. If only a single time period is required, the circuit takes up very little room and there is the possibility of concealing it inside the device being controlled. For example, there is plenty of room inside a typical pottery lamp base for the circuit and the battery.

When the circuit is operated on 6V, it takes 6mA while quiescent. The current required when the relay is energised depends on the resistance of the relay coil. For example, with a high-resistance coil (about 400Ω) the total current is 11mA. With coils of lower resistance, more often found in relays rated to switch mains current at several amps, the current required is greater. For low-current work, and for applications where the relay is energised for a relatively small proportion of the total time, a battery supply is perfectly suitable, and generally more convenient. For longer periods of energising, use a mains-powered power-pack. A 6V 300mA power pack is suitable, since the IC incorporates its own voltage regulator.

It may happen that the controlled device works on DC of a voltage higher than 6V. In this case it makes sense to power the circuit from the same source. The value of R1 may have to be altered. Its value is calculated from:

$$R1 = \frac{5 - V_{SUPPLY}}{I}$$

where I is the current required *by the IC.* This consists of 7mA to power the IC plus the output current which becomes the base current of TR1. This is usually in the order of 5mA.

Having decided on the value of R1, whether or not the timing period is to be variable, and what type of relay is needed, the circuit is best constructed as a whole. Its correct operation is then confirmed by watching the armature of the relay when S1 is pressed. If all is in order, calibrate the setting of VR1 for each position of S2.

The wiring of the relay contacts is the last item in construction. If the relay is to be used for mains current, it is essential that this part of the circuit be kept as far away as possible from the wiring of the rest of the circuit. Connecting wires of appropriate rating must be used. Take care that it is not possible for any bare metal carrying mains current to come into contact with bare metal surfaces of the rest of the circuit. This must not happen even accidentally, for example, if the circuit is dropped on to the floor. Also make sure that surfaces which are well apart while the case is open do not come into contact when the case is closed. If the case is made of metal, it is essential to connect the case to the mains Earth line. Complete all wiring and *close the case* before testing its operation while connected to the mains.

IN ANY EVENT, DO NOT ATTEMPT TO CONSTRUCT THIS PROJECT FOR MAINS SWITCHING UNLESS YOU HAVE HAD PREVIOUS EXPERIENCE OF THIS KIND OF WORK. IF YOU HAVE NOT, CALL ON THE HELP AND ADVICE OF AN EXPERIENCED CONSTRUCTOR.

Chapter 4

USING CLOCK MODULES

Building the dividing chain and display circuits for a basic real-time clock is a fascinating but complicated task. Readers may warm to the challenge of constructing such a project but there is no denying the fact that a mass-produced electronic real-time clock costs far less than the components needed for building its equivalent at home. If you need to access various points in the counting chain, or decode the display outputs, then there is usually no option but to build everything from individual ICs. But, if all that you need is a conventional display of the time, and access to the buzzer output, much effort and money may be saved by using a ready-made clock module.

Several different clock modules are available. Virtually all of them incorporate a crystal oscillator, a dividing chain, logic to drive the liquid crystal display, and logic to generate an alarm signal at a pre-set time. Often there is a snooze timer, which repeats the alarm 5 minutes later if the snooze button is pressed. The more expensive modules have very accurate crystals, giving timing to within 10s per month. They may also have additional facilities such as:

* a seconds timer: the display can be switched to show minutes and seconds;
* a dual clock: two independent clock registers;
* an elapsed-time clock to sound the alarm at the end of a pre-set period: obviously, this function has many applications in process timing;
* various alarm periods: the alarm output is active for pre-settable periods between 5 minutes and, say, 2 hours;
* a counter: counts and displays pulses, counting either up or down.

As an alternative to a purpose-built clock module, consider using the circuitry and display taken from a cheap digital watch or clock. This is discussed in more detail on page 158.

A close relative of the clock module is the timer module. The difference is one of emphasis. A clock module is primarily concerned with registering real time. As indicated above, it may also have facilities for elapsed-time operation. A timer module is intended for elapsed timing, often with several independent timing channels. But usually it also has real-time and alarm modes. When choosing a module for a particular project, you may find that one or other of these classes of module is more appropriate.

Another ready-made module with timing applications is a counter module. Project 13 is an example of the use of such a module.

Timing With a Clock Module

Normally a leaflet is supplied with the module, giving details of the functions available and how to obtain them. Read the leaflet carefully and, where the instructions or advice conflicts with that given below, follow the leaflet rather than this book. The account below is written in general terms but is intended to serve as a guide to the beginner, perhaps faced with a data sheet describing a wide assortment of options in terse technical jargon, or perhaps with no data sheet at all.

We will assume that the module is to be set up for driving one or more devices by means of the output which normally is used to activate the alarm buzzer.

Most modules have an edge-connector with standard 2.54mm spacing, so it may be conveniently mounted in an edge-connector socket, soldered to a rectangle of stripboard. Solder the connector crosswise to the strips, so that each terminal of the clock is connected to one of the strips. Since most modules are intended for building into compact battery powered clocks, and since LCD displays require a current measured in microamps, a single 1.5V button cell is all that is normally required. Figure 4.1 shows one way of mounting the cell. The metal fitting used in one project we constructed was actually part of a small door-bolt set; a search of the shelves in an ironmonger's store will usually produce something suitable that can be used directly or bent or cut to a convenient size and shape. Although a button cell is enough to power the module alone for possibly several thousand hours, you

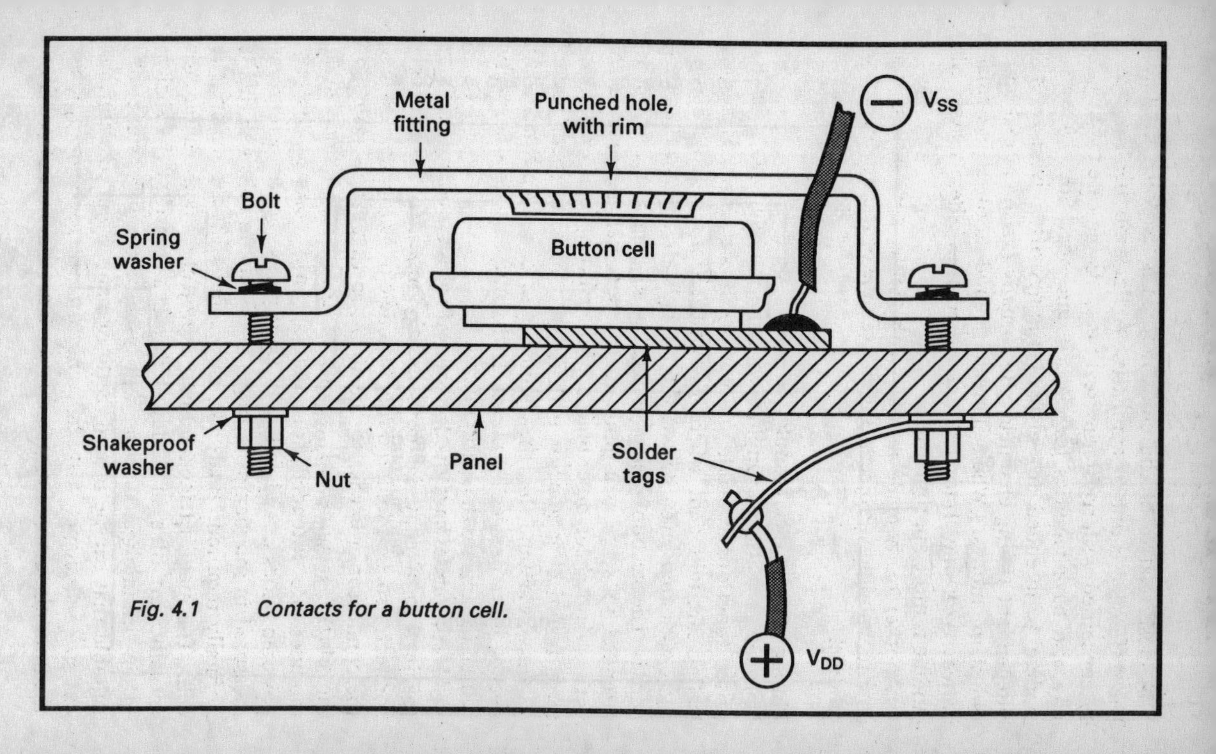

Fig. 4.1 Contacts for a button cell.

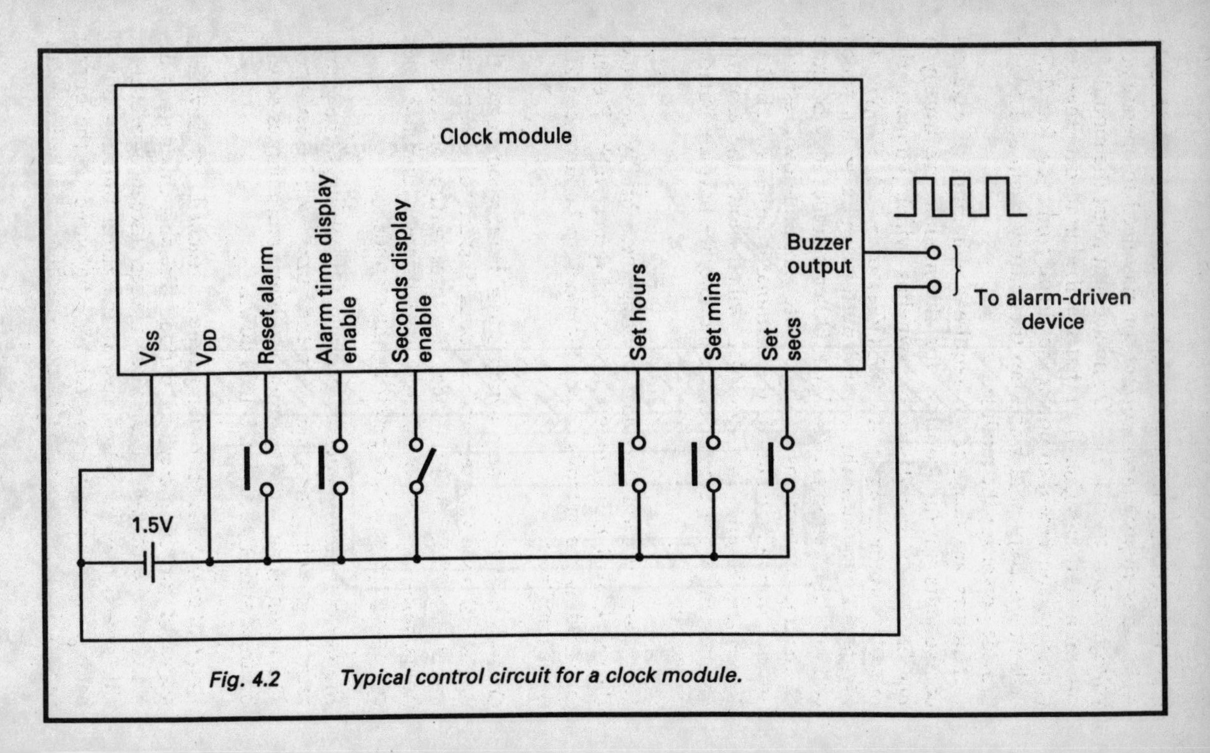

Fig. 4.2 Typical control circuit for a clock module.

may be intending to connect other circuitry to the module which may require more current, or may need to operate at a voltage higher than 1.5V. On no account must the module be run on a voltage higher than that specified in its data sheet, so it may be convenient to power the circuit from, say, four 1.5V cells in a battery holder and tap the battery chain at 1.5V to provide power for the module.

Modules are designed to require a minimum of external components so the controls for the module are usually a number of push-buttons or switches which connect the module terminals either to 0V (V_{SS}) or +1.5V (V_{DD}). In Figure 4.2 we show the control buttons and a switch which connects the terminals to V_{DD}. Other modules may operate by making connections to V_{SS}. Note that pull-down resistors are not normally required; the terminal is either switched to V_{DD} or it is not. In Figure 4.2, which shows the essential connections for a typical clock module, we have six buttons or switches:

Set hours, minutes, seconds: pressing these briefly advances the clock by 1 hour, minute or second respectively. Pressing and holding the buttons causes the clock to be advanced at a more rapid rate.

Seconds display enable: a switch is used here; when closed, the display shows minutes and seconds instead of hours and minutes. When in this mode, the three setting buttons for hours, minutes and seconds may have different functions, such as holding the count, or resetting the seconds.

Alarm-time display enable: pressing this displays the alarm register, showing the time when the buzzer will be activated. The alarm time is set by using the hours and minutes setting buttons while this button is held down.

Reset alarm: when the alarm time is reached, the buzzer is activated for the prescribed period. Pressing this button de-activates the output. If a switch is used instead of a button, this switch may be closed to put the alarm function out of action. Alternatively, a switch may be wired to the buzzer output to disconnect the buzzer or other attached devices.

The only other connection that is likely to be necessary in order to get the module running its basic functions, is to select whether module is to operate as a 12-hour clock or a 24-hour clock. There is often a small pad on the back of the module which may be connected either to V_{SS} or V_{DD} according to which mode of operation is required. The connection may be soldered permanently, or a double-throw switch may be used to make the mode selectable.

Using the Buzzer Output

Modules may have several outputs but the most important is the buzzer output. When the alarm time is reached, this produces a signal intended for driving a small piezo-electric sounder. The signal is usually a high-pitched series of bleeps. Its two limitations are that the signal oscillates between 0V and 1.5V, and that the current available from the output is very small, usually about 100μA. In spite of the low voltage and small current, there are many ways of making use of this signal to trigger other circuits, as described below.

Direct driving: In Figure 4.3 a piezo-electric sounder is driven directly from the buzzer output. Sounders are available in various sizes, which resonate at various frequencies. Since a typical buzzer output gives a 4kHz signal, use a sounder intended to resonate at, or as close as possible to, this frequency. If you simply connect a sounder to the output and leave it lying on the bench, you may very well hear no sound when the alarm is supposed to be sounding. Mounting the sounder correctly makes an enormous difference to the level of sound produced. The sounder should be held firmly by a ring which holds its whole circumference in contact with a rigid panel (Fig. 4.4). Only the rim (the brass outer area, not covered by metallized material) should be held. The central area must be able to vibrate freely; if the panel is not cut away completely over the central area, use a second ring to hold the sounder clear of the panel. Since air vibrations produced at the rear of the panel may travel round to the front and cancel out the air vibrations there, the panel should be as large as conveniently possible.

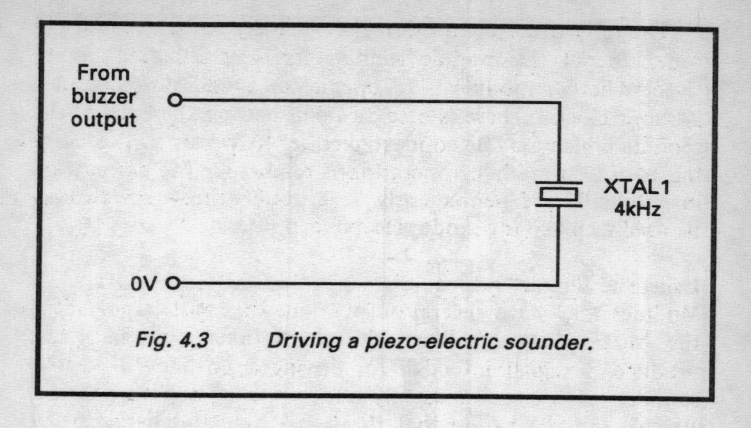

Fig. 4.3 *Driving a piezo-electric sounder.*

Transistor driving: The volume of sound produced by a directly-driven sounder is not great enough to be heard distinctly in a noisy environment. Also, we lose sensitivity of hearing in the higher frequencies as we get older and the sound may be almost inaudible on that account too. Figure 4.5 shows a circuit for increasing the current going to the sounder. As the transistor is switched on and off by the buzzer output, the p.d. across the sounder increases and decreases, causing it to vibrate strongly. The volume may be further increased by driving the circuit from a higher voltage, such as 6V. In Figure 4.5 the transistor is shown as a ZTX300, the type used when designing the circuit. Almost any other type of low-signal npn transistor (e.g. BC108) can be used instead, both in this circuit and in the others described in the chapter.

Driving an AWD: This provides an even louder and very distinctive tone. The audible warning device (Fig. 4.6) is often sold as an 'electronic buzzer'. It requires only a few milliamps (more than can be directly provided from the buzzer output) and operates on a range of voltages, usually from 4.5V up to 15V. The AWD produces its own frequency, which may be higher or lower than that from the clock module and may be intermittent. When the AWD is powered from the transistor switch, it sound intermittently. If the AWD already has

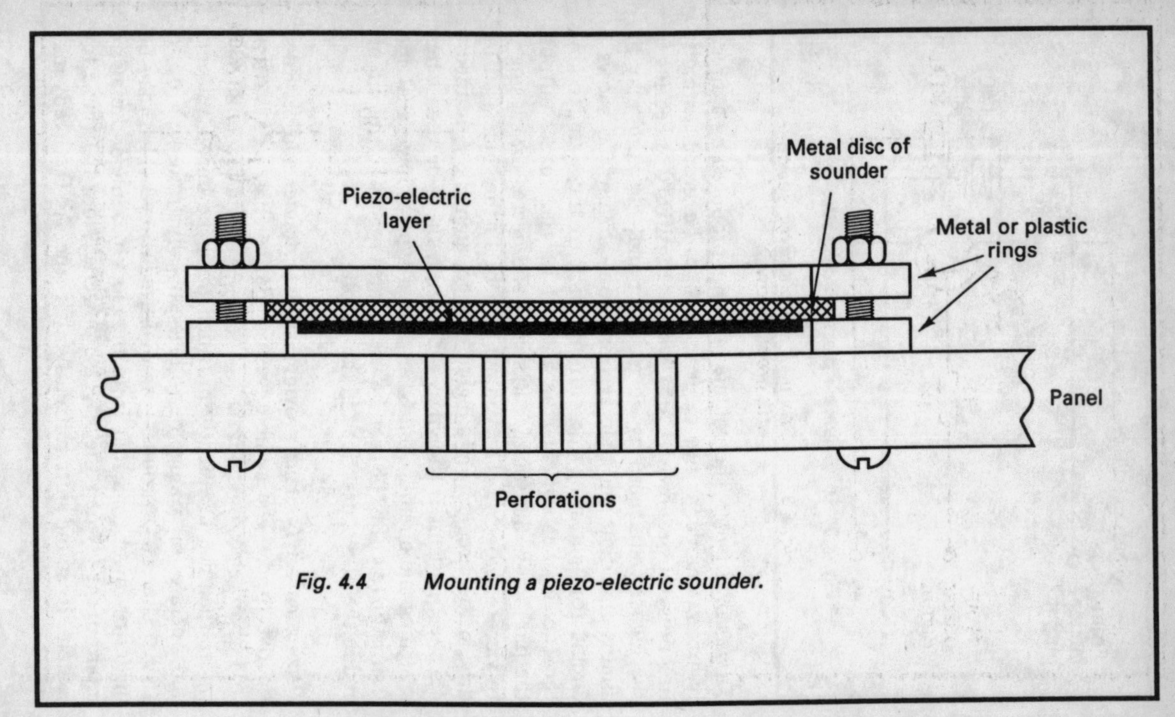

Fig. 4.4 Mounting a piezo-electric sounder.

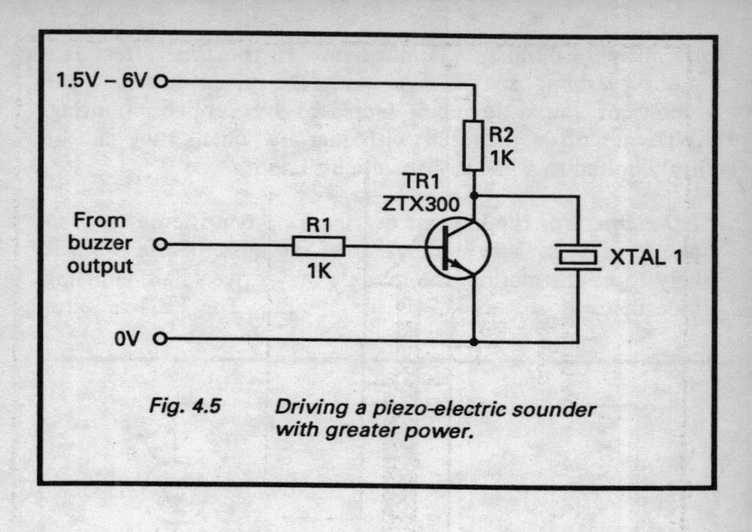

Fig. 4.5 Driving a piezo-electric sounder with greater power.

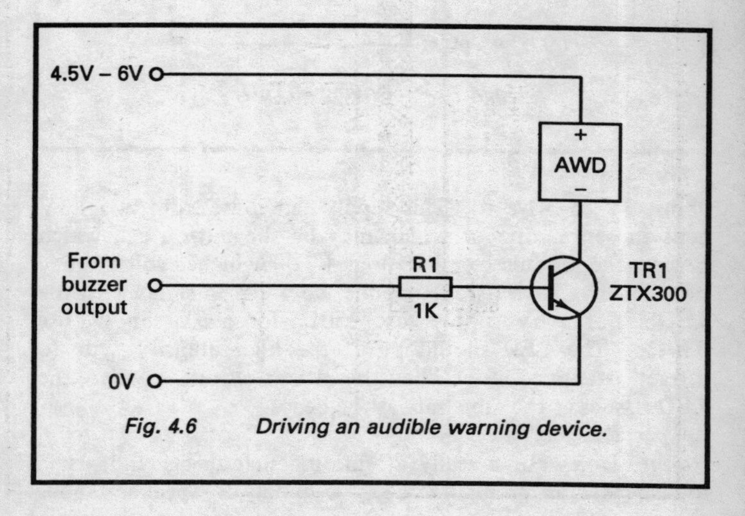

Fig. 4.6 Driving an audible warning device.

intermittent sound programmed into it, the final effect is a unique warbling sound. As with the piezo sounder, the volume of sound is much increased by proper mounting. AWDs are often provided with lugs by which they can be firmly bolted to a panel or the circuit board.

LED alarm: For the hard of hearing, or when the device is to operate in noisy surroundings, or if the noise of the alarm is likely to be distracting, the module may drive a light-emitting diode instead. Figure 4.7 is the circuit. The LED requires

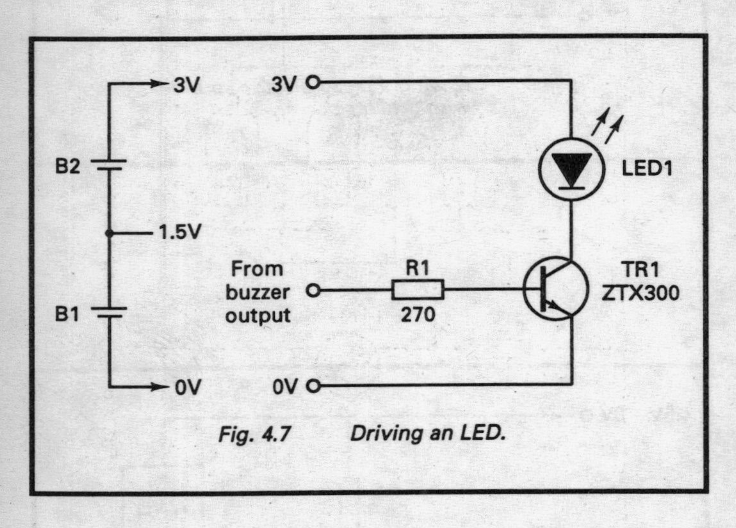

Fig. 4.7 Driving an LED.

about 3V to drive it. This supply can come from two 1.5V cells in series, one of which may be the button cell which powers the module (see left, Fig. 4.7). A higher voltage may be used, but then a resistor must be wired in series with the LED. For a 6V supply, use 150Ω; for a 9V supply, use 330Ω. The LED should be of the high-intensity type to attract attention best. When the buzzer output is active, the LED flashes at the same rate as the beeps.

Room alarm: For a really attention-demanding sound, use a loudspeaker as in Figure 4.8. A miniature speaker (about

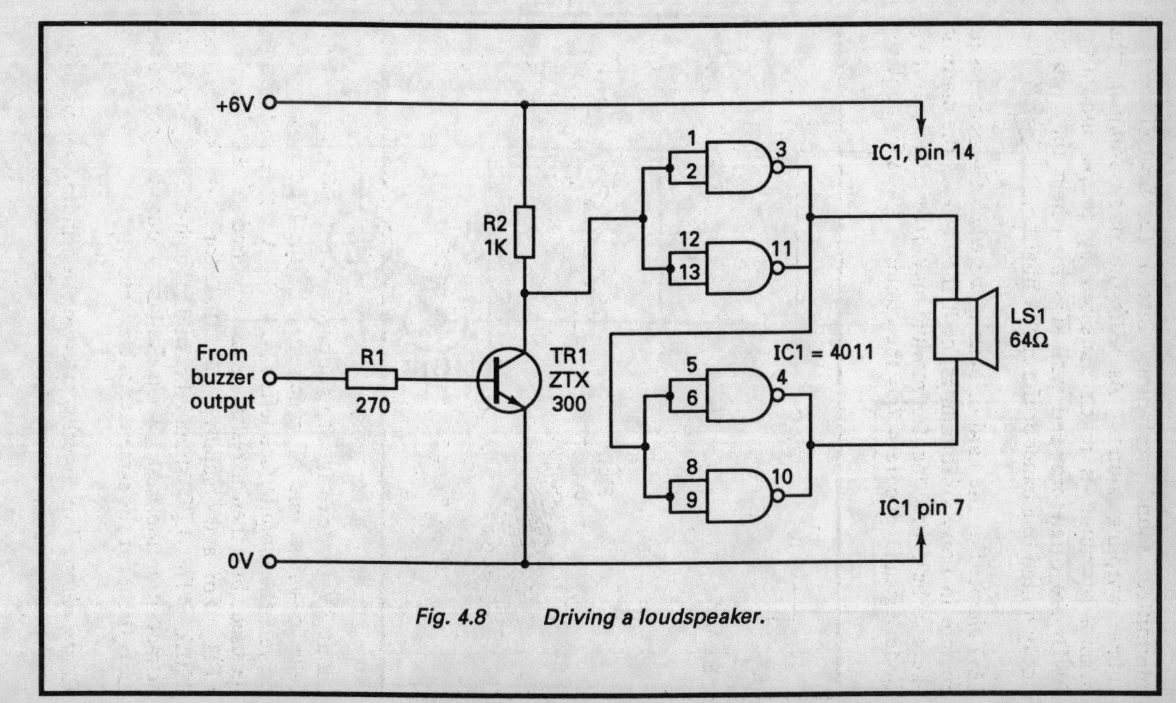

Fig. 4.8 Driving a loudspeaker.

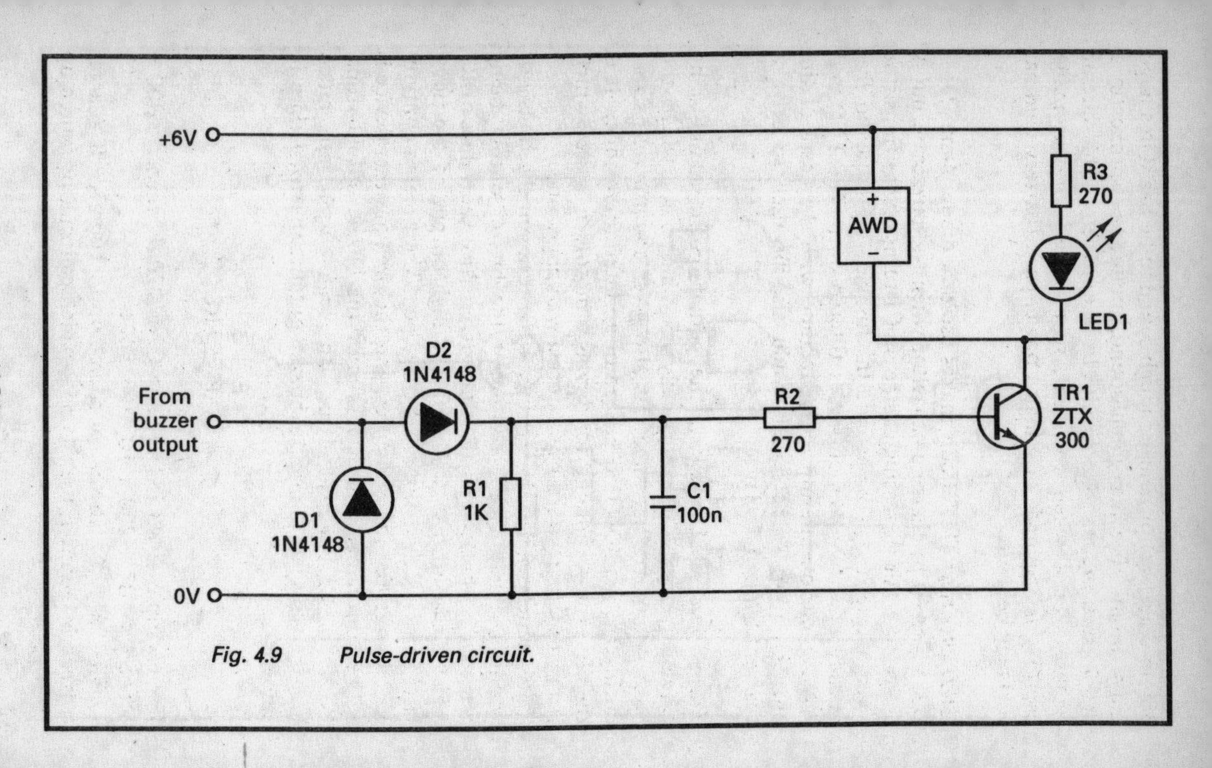

Fig. 4.9 Pulse-driven circuit.

38mm diameter) produces enough sound to be heard in a large noisy room. For maximum sound, mount the speaker in a panel, securing its rim firmly to the panel. This circuit requires 10mA when quiescent, so a battery of reasonable capacity is required, or a mains power-pack (battery eliminator) may be used.

AWD or siren: This circuit makes use of a diode pump (D1–D2, Fig. 4.9) to charge a capacitor when the buzzer output is activated. The increasing charge on C1 turns on the transistor after a fraction of a second. In this circuit, the audio frequency of the buzzer output is filtered out. The LED and AWD come on intermittently, in time with the beeps of the buzzer output. The circuit could also be used to drive a filament lamp or a relay.

Trigger circuit: This allows the period of the alarm to be extended beyond the (typically) 5 minutes for which the buzzer output is activated. It also gives a *continuous* signal during the alarm period instead of an intermittent one. It is therefore more suitable for driving a motor, or a siren which is already programmed to produce a warbling sound.

A diode pump (D1–D2, Fig. 4.10) turns on the transistor within a fraction of a second of the buzzer output being activated. This triggers the timer IC1. With the values of R3 and C2 shown in Figure 4.10, the high output of the timer lasts for 1.1s each time it is triggered. The timer is continually re-triggered for 5 minutes, and the siren or other device is active continuously until 1.1s after the buzzer output stops. If R3 or C2 are made larger, the high output lasts much longer. Given a 5-minute buzzer output, the total time in seconds is:

$$t = 300 + 1.1RC$$

For example, if R3 is 1MΩ and C2 is 220μF, then $t = 300 + 1.1 \times 1 \times 10^6 \times 220 \times 10^{-6} = 542$s.

The 7555 IC can sink or source up to 100mA. If a larger current is required, use the 555, which can sink or source up to 200mA.

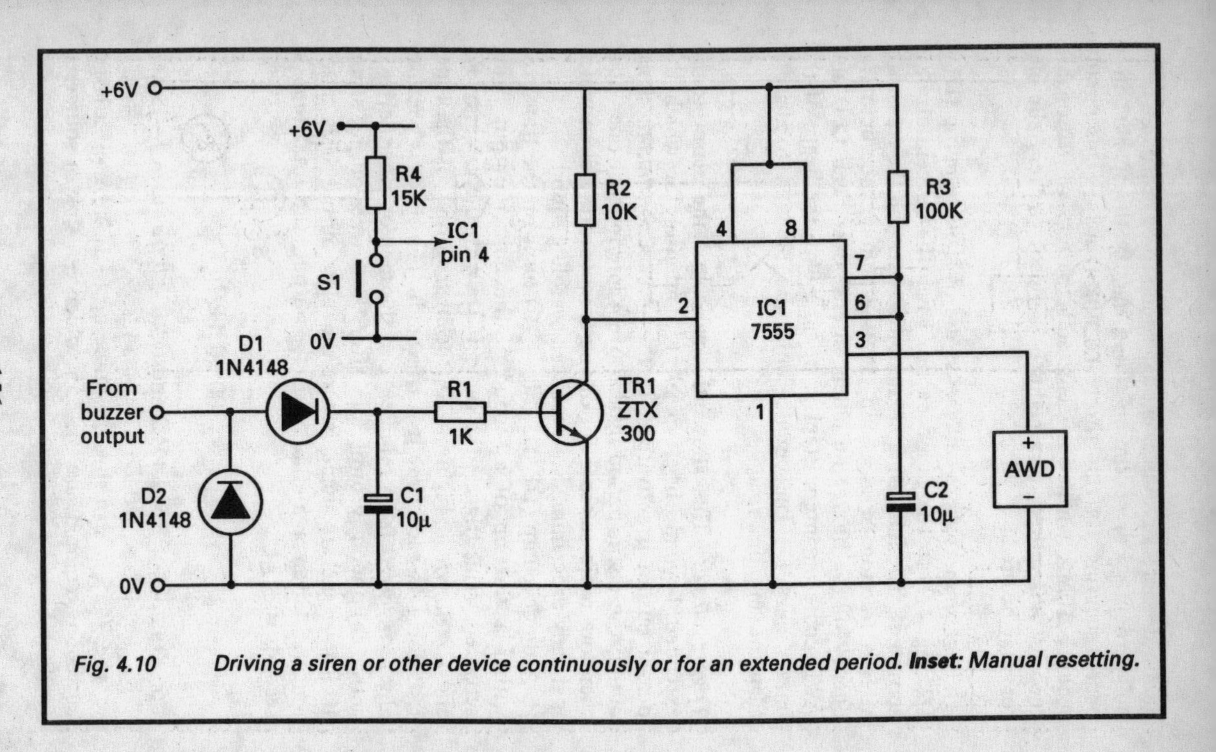

Fig. 4.10 *Driving a siren or other device continuously or for an extended period.* ***Inset:*** *Manual resetting.*

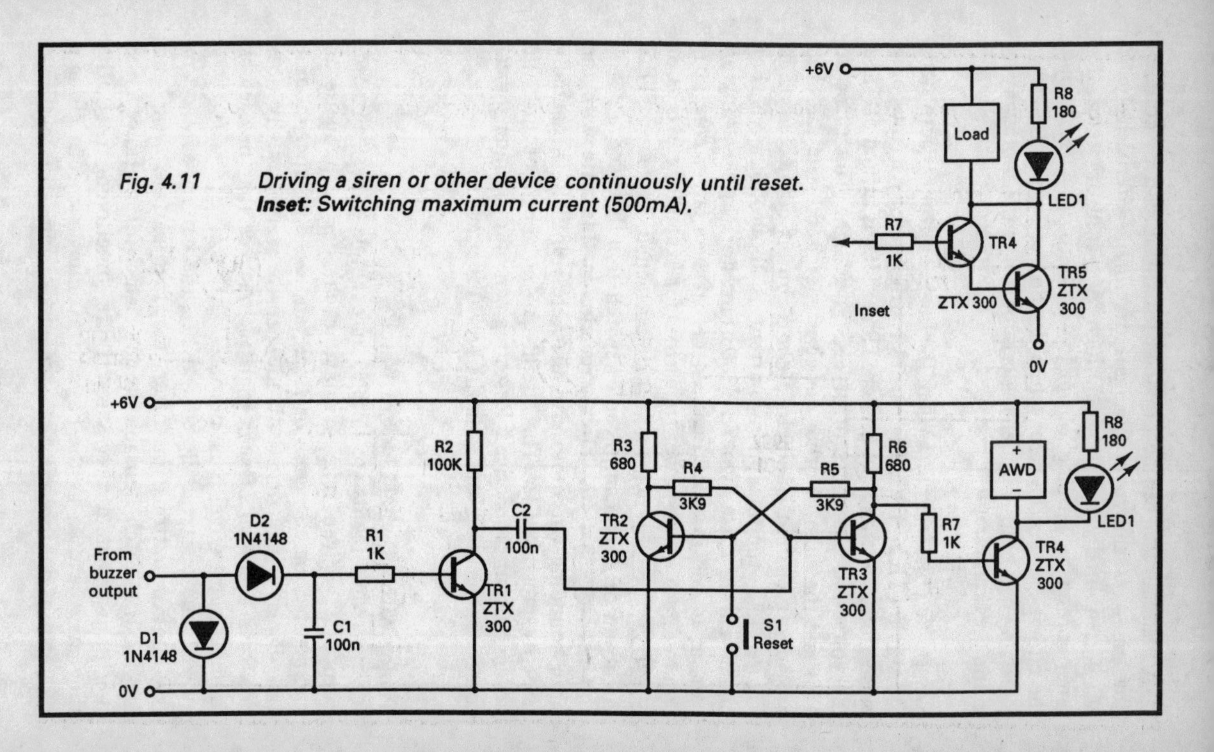

Fig. 4.11 *Driving a siren or other device continuously until reset.*
Inset: *Switching maximum current (500mA).*

A manual reset can be provided for this circuit by connecting pin 4 as shown in the inset drawing. Alternatively, if pin 4 is normally held at logic high by a control circuit, the timer is reset by sending a brief low pulse to pin 4. Note that the circuit can not be reset while the buzzer output is active. Resetting can be put under logical control is the same way as in the previous circuit.

Resettable trigger circuit: When the buzzer output is activated, a bistable (TR2–TR3, Fig. 4.11) is triggered by a low-going pulse from the transistor switch TR1. TR3 is turned off, and the voltage at the collector of TR3 goes high. This turns on TR4 and the siren or other device is energised. The ZTX300 provides a current of up to 500mA, but if connected as in Figure 4.11 the maximum current is about 200mA. For higher current, use two ZTX300 transistors in a Darlington pair, as in the inset of Figure 4.11. If even larger current is required, use a high-power transistor (for example, a BD131 or TIP3055), possibly with a heat sink attached, in place of TR5. A current of several amps can be switched in this way.

Once triggered, the circuit remains in this state with the siren sounding (or motor running, etc.) until it is manually reset by pressing S1. The circuit can not be reset until the buzzer output is inactive. Resetting can be put under logical control in the same way as in the previous circuit.

Timing With a Digital Clock or Watch

If your requirements are simple, for example to have an alarm output at a given time, it may be cheaper to purchase an inexpensive digital watch or clock, and use the timer module and display from that. An inexpensive watch usually does not have a crystal of such high accuracy as that of a clock module, but it serves most purposes.

With the cheapest digital watches, the battery contacts or the control buttons are often the first part to wear out, making the watch unusable in its original form. However, if the timing and display circuits are functioning correctly, they may be used as the basis of a timing project. Using a scrapped watch means that the clock unit costs nothing.

There is a possible advantage in using a watch in preference to a clock module. The typical watch display is smaller than that of a clock module and this may make the unit easier to incorporate into the project.

There is no guarantee that the operation will be entirely satisfactory, for these watches are not intended to be taken apart. But, given a 'worn out' unservicable watch, possibly with a damaged case, there is little to be lost and much to be gained by giving it a second life as part of an electronic timing project.

The exact way to proceed depends on the watch or clock itself but the following remarks apply to most situations. Have a piece of paper and pen at hand to record all essential information as you dismantle the watch. Unless you record everything as you do it, it is all too easy later to be uncertain about a vital connection.

First, remove the cell or battery, noting which contact goes to the positive of the battery and which to the negative. Note also the nominal operating voltage. A single cell gives 1.5V. Prise open the case of the watch with care, since loose parts may drop out and their exact position will not then be known for certain. Make a note of the function buttons, and to which terminals in the timing unit they are connected. This will give you an idea of what functions the watch has available and what switching is required to use them. The most important point to notice for each button is to which power line, positive or negative, or to which terminal of the timing unit, it makes contact when pressed. Note also which terminals on the timing unit connect to the sounder and to the display. Usually the latter is built in to the unit so there will be no connections to be identified.

Summarise all the information you have obtained in a single circuit diagram. Then plan how you intend to use the watch and what contacts and control buttons or switches you will require. From this point on, the procedure is more or less exactly the same as when using a purpose-built clock module, as explained in the previous section of this chapter.

Appendix

TERMINAL CONNECTIONS

Figure A.1 shows the various types of diode used in the projects. The connections shown for light-emitting diodes apply to almost all types, but occasionally a manufacturer produces diodes with the reverse connections. If a diode does not light, reverse it and try again.

In most of the projects we have specified the ZTX300 npn transistor, simply because that is the type used in building most of our prototypes. However, the exact type is not critical and the BC107/108/109 or the 2N3904 may be substituted. Similarly, ZTX500 and 2N3906 may be used interchangeably for the projects in this book, see Figure A.2 for terminal connection details.

Terminal connections of integrated circuits are indicated by pin numbers on the circuit diagrams. The scheme of numbering is illustrated in Figure A.3. Pins are numbered from top left, down the left side and up the right side. Some manufacturers indicate the 'Terminal 1' end by a silver band. The ICs that contain 4 logic gates (4001, 4010 and 4081) have their terminals numbered in the circuit diagrams, but the gates are identical and interchangeable. When you are laying out a pcb or stripboard circuit, you may find it more convenient not to use the gates specified. With a pcb layout, interchanging gates may help to avoid unnecessary crossing of tracks. With a stripboard layout, wiring between gates can sometimes be reduced by not cutting the strip beneath the IC, using it to make a direct connection between terminals on opposite sides of the IC. Similarly, uncut strips can often be used to make connections between adjacent ICs.

Light-emitting diodes (including TIL 38)

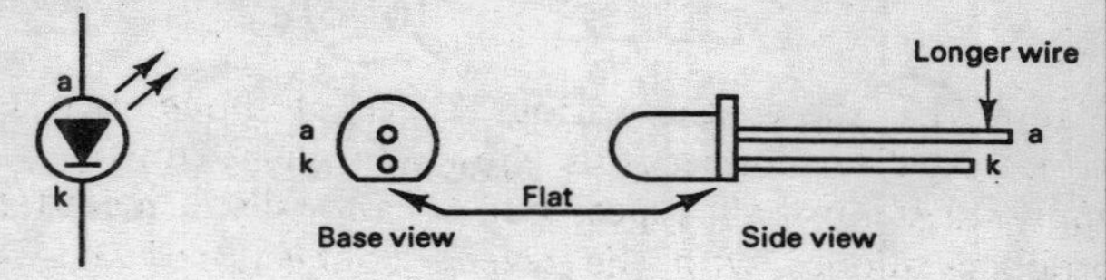

Photo diodes (TIL 100 and similar types)

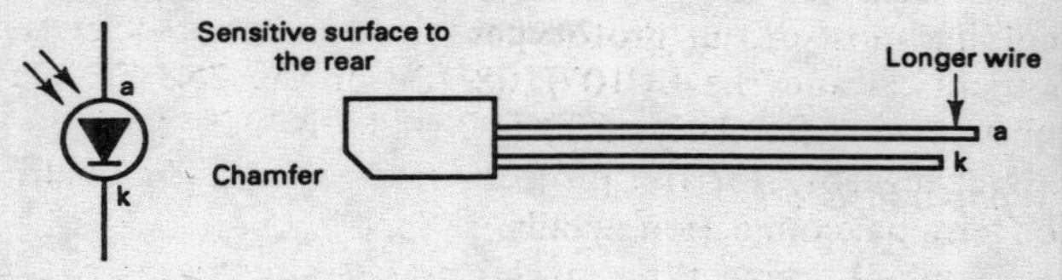

Signal diodes/rectifying diodes

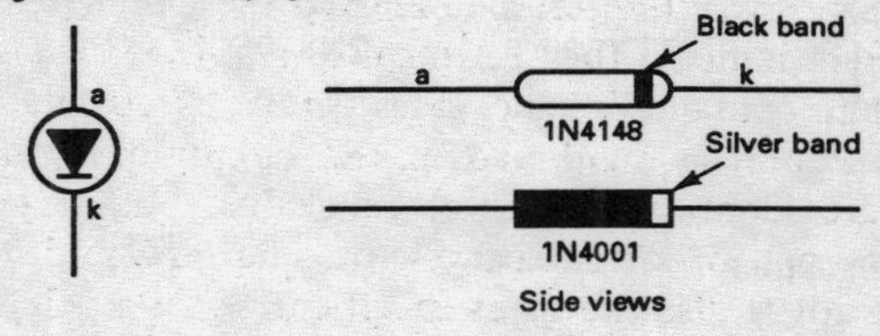

Voltage reference

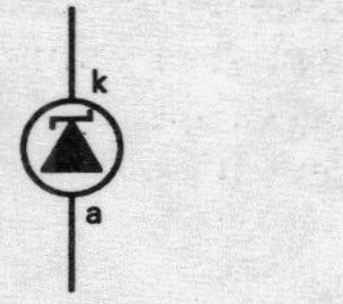

Fig. A.1 *Diode terminal connections: a = anode, k = cathode.*

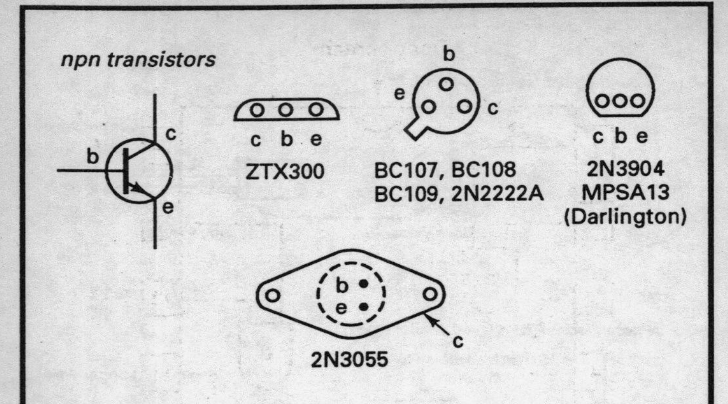

pnp transistors

MOS transistors

Fig. A.2 Transistor terminal connections, all in base view.

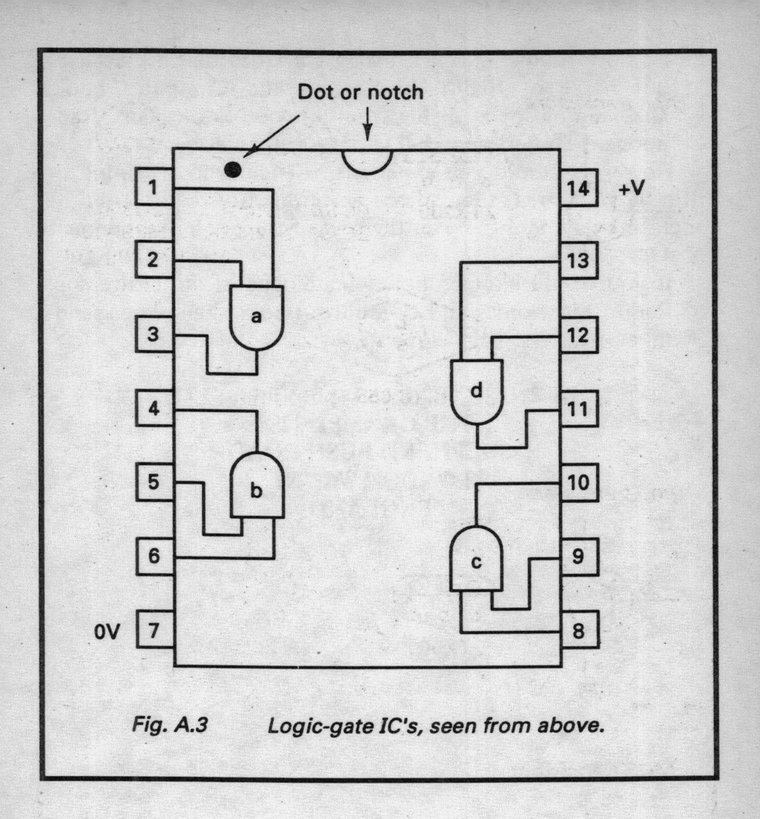

Fig. A.3 *Logic-gate IC's, seen from above.*

Please note following is a list of other titles that are available in our range of Radio, Electronics and Computer books.

These should be available from all good Booksellers, Radio Component Dealers and Mail Order Companies.

However, should you experience difficulty in obtaining any title in your area, then please write directly to the Publisher enclosing payment to cover the cost of the book plus adequate postage.

If you would like a complete catalogue of our entire range of Radio, Electronics and Computer Books then please send a Stamped Addressed Envelope to:

BERNARD BABANI (publishing) LTD
THE GRAMPIANS
SHEPHERD BUSH ROAD
LONDON W6 7NF
ENGLAND